D1533448

The **NEW** CHADD Information and Resource Guide to AD/HD

CHADD®

CHILDREN AND ADULTS WITH
ATTENTION-DEFICIT/
HYPERACTIVITY DISORDER

Contents

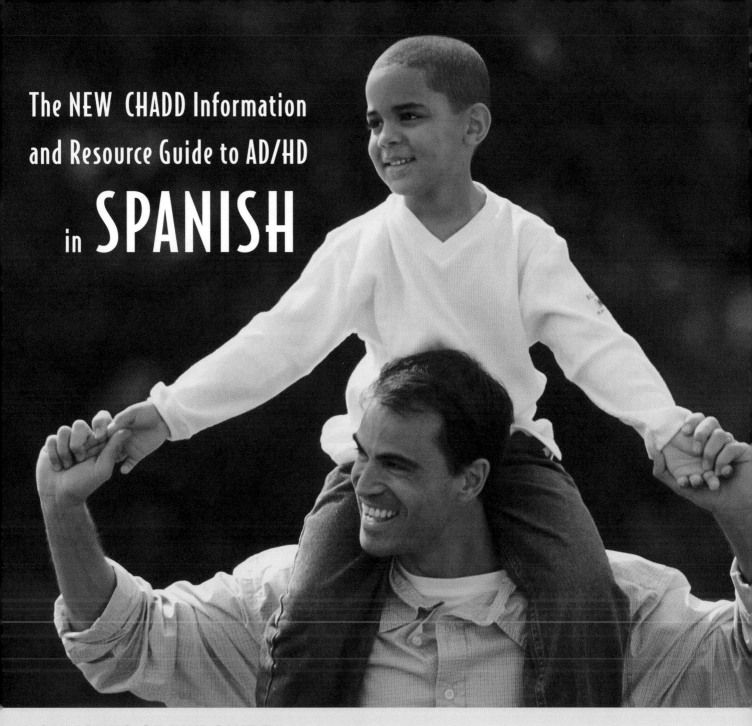

The NEW CHADD Information
and Resource Guide to AD/HD
in **SPANISH**

HIGHLIGHTS OF THE GUIDE (to be published in 2006):

TDA/H

El TDA/H en los Latinos
¿Que sabemos?

El trastorno llamado TDA/H

Evaluando las intervenciónes
complementarias y/o
controvertibles

Lecciónes aprendidas,
mensajes recibidos,
ideas transmítidas

TDA/H en los Niños

Criando a un niño con el
Trastorno por Déficit de
Atención e Hiperactividad

Enfoque en las tareas o
asignaciones

Intervención temprana

Percepciones, creencias y
expectativas de los padres

La reautorización de IDEA

Papás con el TDA/H

TDA/H en los Adolescentes

La transición hacia la escuela
secundaria: Preparándose
para el desafío y el exito

Cuando el TDA/H y el
abuso de sustancias chocan

TDA/H en los Adultos

El diagnóstico del TDA/H en
los adultos

Guías para alcanzar el exito con
el TDA/H en el lugar de trabajo

La administración de
medicamentos para adultos
con TDA/H

CHADD®

CHILDREN AND ADULTS WITH
ATTENTION-DEFICIT/HYPERACTIVITY DISORDER

Chapter 5 • AD/HD in Adults

Chapter 6 • Advocacy and Legal Issues in AD/HD

The information in this resource guide was current and accurate as of September 2005. For updated information on medications, consult the What We Know sheets at www.help4adhd.org/en/about.

CHADD appreciates the unrestricted financial support of Shire US Inc. and UCB Pharma, Inc. to produce this guide.

Chapter 1
Welcome to CHADD

Many Voices as One: CHADD as a Social Movement

By E. Clarke Ross, D.P.A.

You may have turned to CHADD when you first learned your child had AD/HD. You may have felt vulnerable and isolated, and perhaps were in crisis. From CHADD, you obtained a wealth of science-based information on the assessment, treatment, origins and nature of AD/HD. If you were fortunate enough to reside in a community where a well-organized and active CHADD chapter exists, you may have received direct support from peers within your hometown. And if you were really lucky, you lived—and continue to live—in a community with professionals who practice evidence-based approaches to medicine, including multimodal treatment for AD/HD.

CHADD has historically been a membership organization for families dealing with AD/HD, adults with AD/HD, and professionals who treat and support people with AD/HD. As a member of CHADD, you receive numerous benefits such as *Attention!*® magazine, published six times a year. In addition, you can directly access the magazine's archives, participate in "Ask the Expert" chats, discuss AD/HD through members-only chats, participate in CHADD's annual conference at reduced rates, and receive CHADD's *Information and Resource Guide* upon joining. Recently, CHADD created a place on its Web site for professional members to post information about their services. And in 2004, professionals gained access to a special forum focused on "what's hot in professional research literature."

Membership truly is the building block of CHADD. Without you, we could not exist. At the same time, CHADD needs even *more* members to build the social movement so critical to our growth. Assisting people with AD/HD within their communities is CHADD's cause—it's our movement.

Following are eight ways that CHADD functions in this capacity:

1. We are a national leader, advocating for the rights of children with special needs through the Individuals with Disabilities Education Act (IDEA).

2. We operate the National Resource Center on AD/HD, funded by the Centers for Disease Control and Prevention (CDC), which provides reliable science-based information on AD/HD free to the public.

3. We recognize that AD/HD is a lifespan disorder. Regardless of age and regardless of successful treatment, the symptoms and challenges of AD/HD do not completely disappear. CHADD is increasing its focus on lifespan challenges, specifically those faced by adults with AD/HD.

4. We offer to the public a free electronic newsletter with current events and other timely topics. To subscribe, see CHADD's homepage at www.chadd.org.

5. We actively advocate for better health insurance coverage for individuals with mental disorders (this is also known as mental health parity). In addition, we promote health insurance payment for all evidence-based multimodal treatments for AD/HD.

6. We are involved in efforts to prevent juvenile detention and improve services for juveniles with mental disorders who are detained in the juvenile justice system.

7. We have an assertive and high profile public education campaign, the CHADD National AD/HD Education Initiative, to inform the public and its decision makers about the science behind AD/HD.

8. Finally, as CHADD strives to become a more diverse and culturally competent organization and movement, we launched and held 15 educational forums focused on AD/HD for African American and Hispanic/Latino communities during the 2002-04 period in 13 communities.

These are just a few of the most visible efforts currently underway. It is an impressive list of activities and outreach. It is also a modest list reflected by limited resources.

Another challenge is the need to provide face-to-face technical support to our volunteer chapter coordinators. To help them serve as effective advocates, we need to ensure stable and secure chapters in an expanding number of communities. Unfortunately, CHADD currently does not have the resources to take on this challenge.

To have true political impact as a social movement, CHADD needs to represent thousands and thousands of people. This means that we need thousands and thousands of members. We currently have 18,000 paid members. We need many more.

Every voice counts. If you are already a member, thank you. And if not, please consider joining the CHADD family. Together we can make a difference.

E. Clarke Ross, D.P.A. is the Chief Executive Officer of CHADD.

This article first appeared in *Attention!®* magazine, February 2004.

CHADD—It's About Everyone's Life Stories!

By Mary Durheim

CHADD—Children and Adults with Attention-Deficit/Hyperactivity Disorder. That's the name of our organization, but what does it mean to those of us dealing with AD/HD on a daily level?

We assume that most of our readers know about CHADD's beginnings, but my husband constantly says that we should never assume anything. As I started thinking about life stories, I was reminded that CHADD exists because of the life stories experienced by our children, husbands, wives, significant others, siblings, colleagues, neighbors and friends. CHADD is about the struggles and victories that have compelled the nation's researchers to explore the many nuances of the brain associated with AD/HD.

CHADD initially grew out of one family's story. After dealing with years of frustration, guilt and the endless search for "*what works*" at home and at school, this family learned that many other parents were trying to cope with the same problem—a family member with attention-deficit/hyperactivity disorder.

Founded in 1987, CHADD is now a nationwide non-profit organization working for and supporting families and individuals affected by AD/HD. Our local chapters number over 200, and our membership exceeds 18,000 with individuals from all parts of the world. Through informative meetings, publications and the dedication of parents and adults with AD/HD, CHADD members form a close network where we exchange helpful ideas about raising children with AD/HD or living as an adult with AD/HD.

Membership in CHADD connects us with others who share our concerns. CHADD empowers people with AD/HD so that all individuals may better understand and cope with the challenges caused by this disorder.

CHADD and our National Resource Center on AD/HD, funded by the Centers for Disease Control and Prevention, provide information about AD/HD throughout the life span. As our mission statement says, "CHADD works to improve the lives of *all* people affected by AD/HD through: Collaborative Leadership, Advocacy, Research, Education and Support—CHADD Cares!"

CHADD is about each and every one of us and our stories. Whether we need an immediate lifeline to help in a crisis or assistance with ongoing lifespan issues, CHADD connects us with the support and information we need to survive and thrive.

CHADD—giving hope, changing lives!

Thank you for sharing your lives with CHADD.

Mary Durheim is the immediate past president of CHADD, 2003–05.

This article first appeared in *Attention!*® magazine, April 2004.

Life Stories about AD/HD: Listening and Learning

By E. Clarke Ross, D.P.A.

Trying to capture a typical picture of AD/HD is enormously challenging. Some individuals with AD/HD have exceptional IQs; some are of average intelligence. Some children with AD/HD come from two-parent homes and some from single-parent families. Some adults have single types of AD/HD while others have combined types. Some people have co-occurring mental and other health disorders with their AD/HD, and others do not.

AD/HD is non-discriminatory; it affects those who are African American, Hispanic/ Latino, Caucasian, Asian, Native American or a blend of ethnicities. Yet regardless of race, culture, or ethnicity, every person with AD/HD has a story to tell.

Beginning at CHADD's 2000 Annual Conference in Chicago, accelerated with a 2002-2004 contract from the U.S. Center for Mental Health Services (CMHS) and supplemented by a McNeil Consumer and Specialty Pharmaceuticals donation, CHADD has outreached to the African American and Hispanic/Latino communities in more than a dozen cities throughout the country. Our National Resource Center on AD/HD, funded by the Centers for Disease Control and Prevention (CDC), works to ensure that CHADD has Spanish-speaking call center specialists and written materials. And our story bank of life experiences is expanding to better reflect America's diverse and ever-changing landscape.

The challenges faced by people with AD/HD are immense. According to the CDC, roughly half of all children with AD/HD between the ages of 6-11 years have a co-occurring learning disability.[1] In the most definitive clinical trial of school-age children with AD/HD, 69 percent of children with AD/HD have a co-occurring mental disorder.[2] Studies show that children with AD/HD utilize general health services more than three times than other children.[3]

The Surgeon General of the United States[4] and the President's New Freedom Commission on Mental Health have documented that race and culture, both of the treating professional and the potential patient, influence perceptions of AD/HD and other mental disorders. These sobering statistics are complicated by barriers in access to treatment, health insurance obstacles and special education coverage disparities faced by non-white citizens.

In nearly all of my *Attention!*® columns and in other articles I've written, I have shared the story of my 13-year-old son, Andrew. Andrew has the inattentive type of AD/HD. His first neurological problems emerged when he was 11 months old. He has a history of co-occurring health, learning and mental challenges. Given his enormous needs, my wife retired early from the federal government. We continue to receive federal employee health insurance coverage which is among the best health insurance in the nation. Additionally, we live in the Baltimore-Washington, DC area, where the very best medical practitioners reside. We are informed and educated about the science behind the treatment of

AD/HD. We have financial resources that allow us to try complementary interventions for AD/HD not routinely financed by insurance or school. This is our story, but is this a typical CHADD story?

What about the parents who are exhausted by the demands of finding effective treatments and interventions? Or the teenager struggling to fit in but feeling like an outcast? Or the adult who has had to move from job to job due to a string of continuous failures? Are they typical? Yes.

What about the single parent, with three children, with no health insurance, who works long hours in a physically demanding job in a small town with no medical specialists at hand? Or the adult with AD/HD who believes that his/her AD/HD is a blessing, that the condition is not a disorder at all but a difference in the brain chemistry that offers positive attributes that others in society don't have? Are they typical? Again, the answer is yes.

In short, every story and every circumstance is as typical as it is unique. Nothing is more powerful than the life story, and CHADD provides a gathering place to share these stories. As CHADD grows and diversifies, we are working harder than ever to function as an organization where all children, families and adults with AD/HD feel at home. Only through a deeper understanding of our diversities and our similarities can we be the CHADD that represents what is typical.

Notes

1. Centers for Disease Control and Prevention (2002). CDC Vital and Health Statistics. May 2002.

2. National Institute of Mental Health (1999). Multimodal Treatment Study on Children with AD/HD. December 1999.

3. Chan, E.; Zhan, C.; and Homer, C. (2002). "Health Care Use and Costs for Children With Attention-Deficit/Hyperactivity Disorder." *Archives of Pediatric and Adolescent Medicine 156* (May 2002): 504-511; Leibson, C.L.; Katusic, S.L.; Barbares, W.J.; Ransom, J.; and O'Brien, P.C. (2002). "Use and Costs of Medical Care for Children and Adolescents with and without Attention-Deficit/Hyperactivity Disorder," *Journal of the American Medical Association 285* (January 2001): 60-66. The Chan et al article documented that mean average total annual health care costs for all children in the U.S. were $712, while mean average total annual health care costs for children with AD/HD and a co-occurring disorder were $2,367. The Leibson et al article documented health care costs over a nine-year period in Rochester, Minn. While median annual costs for children with AD/HD were $4,306, median annual costs for all children were $1,944.

4. U.S. Department of Health and Human Services (2001). *Mental Health: Culture, Race and Ethnicity—A Supplement to Mental Health: A Report of the Surgeon General.* Rockville, MD: DHHS, Substance Abuse and Mental Health Services Administration, Center for Mental Health Services.

5. New Freedom Commission on Mental Health (July 2003). *Achieving the Promise: Transforming Mental Health Care in America: Final Report.* Rockville, MD. DHHS Pub. No. SMA-03-3832.

E. Clarke Ross, D.P.A. is the Chief Executive Officer of CHADD.

This article first appeared in *Attention!®* magazine, April 2004.

Understanding AD/HD

Overview

Occasionally, we may all have difficulty sitting still, paying attention, or controlling impulsive behavior. But for some children and adults, the problem is so pervasive and persistent that it interferes with their daily lives, including home, school, work, and social settings. If you're reading this article, you probably already recognize some of the symptoms.

AD/HD is a neurobiological disability. It is characterized by developmentally inappropriate impulsivity, inattention, and in some cases, hyperactivity. Although individuals with AD/HD can be very successful in life, without appropriate identification and treatment, AD/HD can have serious consequences such as school failure, depression, conduct disorder, failed relationships, and substance abuse. Early identification and treatment are extremely important.

> Until recent years, it was believed that children outgrew AD/HD in adolescence.

Until recent years, it was believed that children outgrew AD/HD in adolescence. This is because hyperactivity often diminishes during the teen years. However, it is now known that many symptoms continue into adulthood. If the disorder goes undiagnosed or untreated during adulthood, individuals may have trouble at work and in relationships, as well as emotional difficulties, such as anxiety and depression.

Cause

Although AD/HD is one of the best-researched disorders in medicine, its cause nonetheless remains unknown. A great majority of the research suggests a neurobiological basis—an imbalance or deficiency in certain chemicals that regulate the efficiency with which the brain controls behavior. Research also shows that there is a genetic link, thus AD/HD tends to run in families.

Characteristics

AD/HD symptoms arise in early childhood. The disorder is marked by behaviors that are long lasting and evident for at least six months, with onset before age seven. There are three primary subtypes:

AD/HD primarily inattentive type:
- Fails to give close attention to details or makes careless mistakes.
- Has difficulty sustaining attention.
- Does not appear to listen.
- Struggles to follow through on instructions.
- Has difficulty with organization.
- Avoids or dislikes tasks requiring sustained mental effort.
- Is easily distracted.
- Is forgetful in daily activities.

AD/HD primarily hyperactive/impulsive type:
- Fidgets with hands or feet or squirms in chair.
- Has difficulty remaining seated.
- Runs around or climbs excessively.
- Has difficulty engaging in activities quietly.
- Acts as if driven by a motor.
- Talks excessively.
- Blurts out answers before questions have been completed.
- Has difficulty waiting or taking turns.
- Interrupts or intrudes upon others.

AD/HD combined type:
♦ Meets both inattentive and hyperactive/impulsive criteria.

Because everyone shows signs of these behaviors at one time or another, the guidelines for determining whether a person has AD/HD are very specific. In children, the symptoms must be more frequent or severe than in other children of the same age. In adults, the symptoms must be present since childhood and affect one's ability to function in daily life. These behaviors must create significant difficulty in at least two areas of life, such as home, social settings, school, or work.

Diagnosis

In Children and Teens
Determining if a child has AD/HD takes many steps. There is no single test to diagnose the disorder. As a result, a comprehensive evaluation is necessary to establish diagnosis, rule out other causes, and determine the presence or absence of co-existing conditions.

Such an evaluation requires time and effort. It should include a clinical assessment of the child's school, social, and emotional functioning and developmental level. A careful history should be taken from the parents, teachers, and from the child, when appropriate.

Teens with AD/HD present a special challenge, as academic and organizational demands increase. In addition, they face typical adolescent issues: discovering their identity, establishing independence, dealing with peer pressure, exposure to illegal drugs, emerging sexuality, and the challenges of teen driving.

Various professionals are able to diagnose AD/HD, including school and private psychologists, social workers, nurse practitioners, psychiatrists, and other medical doctors. A thorough medical exam by a physician is important. Medication assessment and prescription is the exclusive role of a qualified medical professional, usually a physician.

Regardless of who does the evaluation, use of the *Diagnostic and Statistical Manual IV* (DSM-IV) criteria is necessary. These are checklists used for rating AD/HD symptoms and ruling out other disorders.

In Adults
Growing up with undiagnosed AD/HD can have devastating effects, with adults often thinking of themselves as "lazy," "crazy," or "stupid." As a result, proper diagnosis can be profoundly healing, putting present difficulties into perspective and making sense of lifelong symptoms.

A comprehensive evaluation for AD/HD is best made by clinicians with experience in the disorder. This team may include a behavioral neurologist, psychiatrist, or a clinical or educational psychologist. A comprehensive evaluation should include (1) surveying past and present AD/HD symptoms; and (2) developmental, medical and psychiatric history; including school and work experiences, social skills, and the general ability to meet the demands of daily life. Ideally, the exam should include several sources of information, such as a parent or significant other. An adult evaluation should also use the DSM-IV symptom rating scales.

> A comprehensive evaluation for AD/HD is best made by clinicians with experience in the disorder.

Treatment

In Children and Teens
Treating AD/HD in children requires positive behavior intervention strategies as well as educational, psychological and medical interventions. This team approach to treatment is called "multimodal" and includes:
♦ parent and child education about diagnosis and treatment,
♦ behavior management techniques,

♦ medication, and

♦ school programming and supports.

Treatment should be tailored to the unique needs of each child and family.

Positive behavior intervention can be critical. The most important techniques are consistency and positive reinforcement, in which the child is rewarded for desired behavior. Classroom success may require a range of interventions, from making minor adjustments in the regular classroom to requiring special education programs. For many children with AD/HD, medication may be an integral part of treatment. "Psychostimulant" compounds are the most widely used to improve symptoms, with between 70 to 80 percent of children responding positively to them.

In Adults

Treatment for adults with AD/HD is also multimodal. The team includes health care professionals, the adult and immediate family —with accurate information about the disorder being critical to all concerned. Adults can benefit from learning to structure their environments as well as from vocational counseling. Short or long-term psychotherapy can also help.

Medication may be part of the treatment to improve the symptoms of AD/HD. Psychostimulant medication can be effective in adults, with many reporting they are able to gain more control and organization in their lives.

Symptoms vs. Impairment

Sometimes an individual has all of the symptoms of AD/HD, yet is very successful at school and at home. In other words, he does not appear to be impaired by the symptoms. Clinicians need to carefully consider the question of impairment when making the diagnosis of AD/HD. Impairment refers to the negative impact of AD/HD on day to day functioning. The diagnostic process should consist not only of a symptom count and patient history, but of a discussion about impairment as well.

Why is the issue of impairment important? If a person is not impaired, treatment may not be necessary. The diagnostic manual that all clinicians use states that "some impairment from the symptoms is present in two or more settings (such as school, work, or home)." It states that "there must be clear evidence of clinically significant impairment in social, academic or occupational functioning." Part of the diagnostic process is also to determine the severity of the impairment (mild, moderate, or severe).

Impairments from AD/HD are often related to problems of self control and self regulation. If a child is unable to learn in class because of inattention and impulsiveness, this would be an impairment in academic functioning. If an adult is unable to maintain a relationship with a significant other because of poor self control and problems with executive functioning, this would be an impairment of social functioning. It is important for parents and those with AD/HD to understand the role of impairment in diagnostic and treatment decisions. Clinicians need reliable and regular feedback about the level of impairment and the areas of life affected. Working together, the goal of treatment is to reduce or eliminate the impairment caused by AD/HD.

Note: This information was drawn from "Symptoms vs. Impairment: The Role of Impairment in Diagnosing AD/HD," by Sam Goldstein, *Attention!* ® June 2003.

AD/HD Myths: Science Over Cynicism

By Phyllis Anne Teeter Ellison, Ed.D.

Public perceptions of attention-deficit hyperactivity disorder (AD/HD) are replete with myths, misconceptions and misinformation about the nature, course and treatment of the disorder. Popular misconceptions assert that AD/HD is not a disorder or—at minimum—is a benign one that is over-diagnosed. Critics often claim that children are needlessly medicated by parents who have not properly managed their unruly, unmotivated or underachieving children, or who are looking for an academic advantage (e.g., testing or classroom accommodations) in competitive, high-stakes educational environments. Some suggest that "a growing intolerance of childhood playfulness may in fact be leading to more and more children being labeled with AD/HD" (Panksepp, 1998, p. 91). Critics rarely present evidence-based arguments and frequently allege that professionals are harming otherwise normal children by diagnosing and treating AD/HD.

While barriers to treatment have been reduced in recent years, there is a climate of blame, shame, embarrassment and stigma that discourages some from seeking help for debilitating mental health disorders, including AD/HD. There is compelling evidence that a large number of youths with a variety of mental disorders, including AD/HD, are not being served, are inadequately served or are inappropriately served in communities across the country (Surgeon General's Report, 2001; Jensen et al., 1999; MTA, 1999). The *Executive Summary on Mental Health: Culture, Race and Ethnicity, a Supplement to the Surgeon General's Report* (2001) indicates that 75–80 percent of children and youths with mental health illnesses do not receive needed services. Misinformation often demonizes those in need of treatment for AD/HD and may discourage individuals from seeking appropriate care. Parents may avoid professional help because they fear being labeled poor parents who needlessly medicate their children. Parents of children with AD/HD are often accused of seeking to medicate overly playful, non-compliant or mildly disruptive children. More likely, parents are struggling to help their children cope with a serious constellation of problems and are seeking help because previous attempts to reduce the impact of AD/HD have failed. Chronic, untreated disorders such as AD/HD are costly to the individual, family and society (Leibson et al., 2001). Parents generally seek professional help for AD/HD after a great deal of deliberation, consternation and past failures. This article will summarize and attempt to dispel some of the common misconceptions about AD/HD.

Myth #1—AD/HD is Not a Real Disorder

This is a common refrain expressed by individuals who assert that the psychiatric community, in concert with pharmaceutical companies, created AD/HD to drum up business for private practices and to increase profits for drug companies. According to the National Institutes of Health, the Surgeon General of the United States, and an international community of clinical researchers, psychiatrists and physicians, there is general consensus that AD/HD is a valid disorder with severe, life-long consequences (NIH, 2000; U.S. Surgeon General's Report, 2001). Studies over the past 100 years demonstrate that AD/HD is a chronic disorder that has a negative impact on virtually every aspect of daily social, emotional, academic and work functioning (Barkley, 1998). Studies show that children with AD/HD have higher rates of other psychiatric disorders, higher frequency of hospitalizations, emergency room visits and total medical costs, compared to individuals without AD/HD (Liebson et al., 2001).

> It is difficult to find evidence that AD/HD is over-diagnosed or that stimulant medications are over-prescribed.

Adolescent outcomes of children with AD/HD show that they are more likely to drop out of school, not complete college, have fewer friends and participate in antisocial activities than children without AD/HD (Barkley, Fischer, Edelbrock, & Smallish, 1990). Rates of cigarette, alcohol and marijuana use among those with both AD/HD and conduct disorders were two to five times higher than in adolescents with AD/HD alone or for those without it. Later in life, adults with AD/HD have higher rates of employment difficulties, depression and personality disorders, auto accidents, sexually transmitted diseases and teen pregnancies, compared to individuals without AD/HD (Fischer, Barkley, Smallish, & Fletcher, 2002). Overwhelming evidence suggests that AD/HD is a real disorder with serious consequences.

Myth #2—AD/HD is a Disorder of Childhood

Early discussions of AD/HD theorized that individuals outgrew the disorder (Ingram, Hechtman, & Morgenstein, 1999). This notion has been dispelled by long-term studies showing that anywhere from 70–80 percent of children with AD/HD exhibit significant signs of restlessness and distractibility into adolescence and young adulthood, while a large percentage suffer co-morbid psychiatric disorders, academic failure, and social isolation and/or rejection (Barkley et al., 1990; Barkley, 1998). Research estimates that 1.5–2 percent of adults have AD/HD (Hunt, 1997), and between 2 and 6 percent of adolescents have AD/HD (Murphy & Barkley, 1996). Cuffe et al. (2001) found that children with persistent AD/HD have more severe AD/HD and adverse risk factors later in life. Adverse factors impact the expression of AD/HD and increase the risk for associated disorders that compromise adjustment over the lifespan. Thus, AD/HD is a lifelong disorder that requires a developmental framework for appropriate diagnosis and treatment (Teeter, 1998).

Myth #3—AD/HD is Over-Diagnosed

Critics claim that AD/HD is over-diagnosed and that many children with the diagnosis do not have AD/HD. Despite these claims, it is difficult to find evidence that AD/HD is over-diagnosed or that stimulant medications are over-prescribed (Jensen et al., 1999). Moreover, Jensen et al. (1999) suggest that in "some cases AD/HD may be undiagnosed and/or untreated" (p. 798). Although this is a complex problem, prevalence rates of AD/HD range from 2–9 percent (Barkley, 1998). Rates vary depending on the rating scales employed, the criteria used to make a diagnosis, the use of cut-off scores, and changes in diagnostic criteria. Prevalence rates increased when AD/HD—predominately inattentive type (AD/HD-I)—was added to the DSM-IV (Wolraich et al., 1996).

Changes in special education legislation in the early 1990s increased general awareness of AD/HD as a handicapping condition and provided the legal basis for the diagnosis and treatment of AD/HD in the school setting.

These legal mandates have increased the number of school-based services available to children with AD/HD and may have inadvertently led some to conclude that AD/HD is a new disorder that is overdiagnosed.

Myth #4—Children with AD/HD are Over-Medicated

"Critics of stimulant treatment for youths with attention-deficit/hyperactivity disorder (AD/HD) have increased their rhetoric of late, contending that the leading medication for it, Ritalin, is vastly overprescribed" (Safer, 2000, p. 55). There are seemingly contradictory data that contribute to this confusion—e.g., a steady increase in stimulant use, although most school-aged children with AD/HD are not medicated in the community (Jensen et al., 1999).

Although there has been an increase in the rate of prescriptions for stimulants and an increase in the production of methylphenidate, "little is known about why these increases are occurring" (Jensen et al., 1999, p. 797). "Most researchers believe that much of the increased use of stimulants reflects better diagnosis and more effective treatment of a prevalent disorder" (Surgeon General's Report, 2001, p. 149). Others suggest that the changes may be a function of increased prescription rates for girls and teens with AD/HD (Safer, 2000). The percentage of children who receive medication of any kind is small. Goldman et al. (1998) reported that 2.8 percent of elementary school-aged students were on medication, and that stimulants accounted for 99 percent of the prescribed medications. So while there has been an increase in the number of prescriptions, a relatively low overall rate of stimulant use is reported in school-aged children. Furthermore, physicians in the community tend to use less than optimal doses, have fewer follow-up monitoring sessions, and achieve less medication compliance than recommended by the MTA study (Jensen et al., 2001).

Myth #5—Poor Parenting Causes AD/HD

This misconception may be the most difficult to dispel because parenting characteristics (i.e., being critical, commanding, negative) and poor management do exacerbate AD/HD and increase the risk for co-morbid disorders (e.g., oppositional defiance and conduct disorders; Barkley, 1998). Twin studies exploring the contribution of environmental factors (e.g., parenting practices, parental psychopathology) find that genetic factors, and not a shared environment, account for the greatest variance in AD/HD symptoms—about 80 percent (Goodman & Stevenson, 1989). While management difficulties influence parent-child conflicts and the maintenance of hyperactivity and oppositional problems in young children (Barkley et al., 1990), Barkley (1998) concludes that "theories of causation of AD/HD can no longer be based solely or even primarily on social factors, such as parental characteristics, caregiving abilities, child management or other family environmental factors" (p. 176).

Other factors may play a causal role in the individual differences in symptoms of AD/HD, including exposure to environmental toxins (e.g., elevated blood lead, prenatal exposure to alcohol and tobacco smoke), but not all children exposed to these risk factors have high rates of hyperactivity, nor do all children with AD/HD have these risk factors (Barkley, 1998). Furthermore, prenatal and birth complications are not more frequent in children with AD/HD compared to normal children. Although other factors (e.g., family adversity, poverty, educational/occupational status, home environment, poor nutrition, environmental toxins, ineffective childrearing practices) *do not appear* to have a significant contribution to the development of AD/HD symptoms (see Barkley, 1998 for a review), these factors contribute to co-morbid disorders and complicate treatment effectiveness.

Johnston and Freeman (2002) identified a number of inaccurate or non-scientifically based parent beliefs about the causes of AD/HD including: allergic reactions or sensitivity to foods, family problems like alcoholism or marital discord, high sugar consumption, ineffective discipline, lazy learning habits, a lack of motivation, etc. In this study, inaccurate or "false beliefs" were associated with parental attributions that children were responsible for their AD/HD symptoms (symptoms are intentional and children can control their symptoms) and the use of less effective treatment (e.g., diet control). Parent perceptions and beliefs about the nature of AD/HD are related to treatment outcome (Hoza et al., 2000). Furthermore, attributions that AD/HD symptoms are intentional and controllable often result in harsh, critical and punitive parenting practices (Johnston & Patenaude, 1994). These misperceptions are frequently addressed in parent training components of multimodal treatment plans.

> Evidence suggests that minority children are not over medicated and may actually be underserved for AD/HD.

Myth #6—Minority Children Are Over-Diagnosed with AD/HD and Are Over-Medicated

Access to diagnosis and treatment of mental disorders varies depending on gender, race and social economic status (SES), but not in the way one might predict. *Mental Health: Culture, Race and Ethnicity from the Report of the Surgeon General* (2001) shows that African American youths are over-represented in arrests, detentions, incarcerations, classes for emotional disturbance and the child welfare system. However, African Americans do not appear to receive needed treatment for AD/HD or for other mental health disorders.

Research investigating AD/HD in African American youths is also sparse. In a study of public school children and youths in Florida, Bussing et al. (1998) found that service delivery to African American children was deficient even though there was no evidence that the incidence rate of AD/HD was lower than those reported in whites. Bussing et al. (1998) found that: (1) only 50 percent of children with AD/HD were receiving treatment, (2) girls were underserved at a rate three times lower than boys, and (3) whites were three times more likely to be referred compared to African American children. In the few studies exploring medication rates across races, ethnic minority children are 2–2.5 times less likely to be medicated for AD/HD than white children (Safer & Malever, 2000).

Access to treatment is affected by a number of factors unrelated to need including: (1) a lack of perceived need; (2) system barriers including availability, cost and language; (3) concerns that their children would be taken from the home if parents seek services; (4) stigma associated with seeking help for mental illnesses; and, (5) cost of treatment, lack of adequate reimbursement, length of treatment and cost of medication (Bussing et al., 1998). Furthermore, African Americans are less likely to receive care and are more likely to leave mental health treatment prematurely. Evidence suggests that minority children are not over medicated and may actually be underserved for AD/HD.

Myth #7—Girls Have Lower Rates and Less Severe AD/HD than Boys

According to the *Surgeon General's Report on Mental Health* (2001), girls are less likely to receive a diagnosis of and treatment for AD/HD compared to boys despite need. Gaub and Carlson (1997) found that girls with AD/HD have greater intellectual impairment, but lower rates of hyperactivity and externalizing disorders compared to boys. Girls with AD/HD have more severe internalizing disorders than boys, and both show more similarities than differences in symptoms and treatment needs. Biederman et al. (1999) found that girls with AD/HD were more likely to have conduct problems, mood and anxiety disorders, lower IQ, and more impairment on social, family and school functioning than non-referred girls. However, conduct problems occurred less in girls than in boys with AD/HD, which may account for lower referral rates in community and school samples. Girls in clinic samples also had high rates of substance abuse, alcohol, drug and cigarette use, and were at an increased risk for panic and obsessive compulsive disorders (Biederman et al., 1999).

Finally, Rucklidge and Tanner (2001) found that girls with AD/HD were more impaired than a control group on measures of depression, anxiety, self-esteem, overall symptom distress and stress. Girls with AD/HD reported strained relationships with teachers, thoughts of suicide and past episodes of self-harm.

Compared to boys with AD/HD, girls with AD/HD reported higher rates of overall distress, anxiety and depression. They also demonstrated more hyperactivity and conduct and cognitive deficits. Parents and teachers noted higher rates of inattention, hyperactivity, oppositional defiance, conduct problems, social difficulties, depression and anxiety. Girls may report more distress than boys, and they "may be more affected by environmental factors than males with AD/HD" (Rucklidge & Tanner, 2001). Thus, gender differences need to be more fully addressed in longitudinal and treatment studies.

Myths and inaccurate information about AD/HD should be dispelled by scientific findings. However, popularly held "false beliefs," which are often perpetuated by emotional or unexamined arguments, do more harm than good. They do little to advance our knowledge and do a lot to discourage individuals from seeking help and using effective treatments for AD/HD that have undergone rigorous scientific scrutiny.

Notes

Barkley, R. A., (1998). *Attention-deficit hyperactivity disorder: A handbook for diagnosis and treatment.* New York: Guildford Press.

Barkley, R. A., Fischer, M., Edelbrock, C., & Smallish, L. (1990). The adolescent outcome of hyperactive children diagnosed by research criteria: I. An 8-year prospective follow-up study. *Journal of the American Academy of Child & Adolescent Psychiatry, 29,* 546–557.

Biederman, J., Faraone, S., Mick, E., Williamson, S., Wilens, T., Spencer, T., Weber, W., Jettson, J. Kraus, I., Pert, J., & Zallen, B. (1999). Clinical correlates of AD/HD in females: Findings from a large group of girls ascertained from pediatric and psychiatric referral sources. *Journal of the American Academy of Child and Adolescent Psychiatry, 38,* 966–975.

Bussing, R., Zima, B.T., Perwien, A.R., Belin, T.R., & Widawski, M. (1998). Children in special education programs: Attention deficit hyperactivity disorder, use of services and unmet needs. *American Journal of Public Health, 88,* 880–886.

Cuffe, S.P., McKeown, R., Jackson, K., Addy, S., Abramson, R., & Garrison, C. (2001). Prevalence of attention-deficit/hyperactivity disorder in a community of older adolescents. *Journal of the American Academy of Child and Adolescent Psychiatry, 40,* 1037–1044.

Fischer, M., Barkley, R. A., Smallish, L., & Fletcher, K. (2002). Young adult follow-up of hyperactive children: Self-reported psychiatric disorders, comorbidity, and the role of childhood conduct problems and teen CD. *Journal of Abnormal Child Psychology, 30,* 463–475.

Goldman, L.S., Genel, M., Bezman, R.J., & Slanetz, P.J. (1998). Diagnosis and treatment of attention-deficit/hyperactivity disorder in children and adolescents. Council on Scientific Affairs, American Medical Association. *Journal of the American Medical Association, 297,* 1100–1107.

Goodman, R. & Stevenson, J. (1989). A twin study of hyperactivity: II. The aetiological role of genes, family relationships, and perinatal adversity. *Journal of Child Psychology and Psychiatry, 30,* 691–709.

Gaub, M., & Carlson, C. L. (1997). Gender differences in AD/HD: A metaanalysis and critical review. *Journal of the American Academy of Child and Adolescent Psychiatry, 36,* 1036–1045.

Hoza, B., Owens, J.S., Pelham, W.E., Swanson, J.M., Conners, C.K., Hinshaw, S., Arnold, L., & Kraemer, H.C. (2000). Parent cognitions as predictors of child treatment response in attention-deficit/hyperactivity disorder. *Journal of Abnormal Child Psychology, 28,* 569–583.

Hunt, R.D. (1997). Nosology, neurobiology, and clinical patterns of AD/HD in adults. *Psychiatry Annals, 27,* 572–581.

Ingram, S., Hechtman, L., & Morgenstern, G. (1999). Outcome issues in AD/HD: Adolescent and adult long-term outcome. *Mental Retardation and Developmental Disabilities Research Reviews, 5,* 243–250.

Jensen, P.S., Hinshaw, S., Swanson, J., Greenhill, L., Conners, K., Arnold, E. et al. (2001). Findings from the NIMH multimodal treatment study of AD/HD (MTA): Implications and applications for primary care providers. *Developmental and Behavioral Pediatrics, 22,* 60–73.

Jensen, P.S., Kettle, L., Roper, M.T., Sloan, M.T., Dulcan, M.K., Hoven, C., Bird, H., Bauermister, J., & Payne, J. (1999). Are stimulants overprescribed? Treatment of AD/HD in four U.S. communities. *Journal of the American Academy of Child and Adolescent Psychiatry, 38,* 797–804.

Johnston, C., & Freeman, W. (2002). Parent's beliefs about AD/HD: Implications for assessment and treatment. *AD/HD Report, 10,* (6–9).

Johnston, C., & Paternaude, R. (1994). Parent attributions for inattentiveoveractive and oppositional-defiant child behaviors. *Cognitive Therapy and Research, 18,* 261–275.

Leibson, C.L., Katusic, S.K., Barbaresi, W.J., Ransom, J., & O'Brien, P.C. (2001). Use and cost of medical care for children and adolescents with and without attention-deficit/hyperactivity disorder. *JAMA, 285,* 60–66.

MTA Cooperative Group. (1999). A 14-month randomized clinical trial of treatment strategies for attention-deficit/hyperactivity disorder. *Archives of General Psychiatry, 56,* 1073–1086.

Murphy, K., & Barkley, R.A. (1996). Attention deficit hyperactivity disorder in adults. Comprehensive *Psychiatry, 37,* 393–401.

National Institutes of Health Consensus Development Conference Statement: Diagnosis and Treatment of Attention Deficit/Hyperactivity Disorder (AD/HD) (2000). *Journal of the American Academy of Child and Adolescent Psychiatry, 39,* 182–193.

Panksepp, J. (1998). Attention deficit hyperactivity disorders, psychostimulants, and intolerance of child playfulness: A tragedy in the making? *Current Directions in Psychological Science, 7,* 91–98.

Rucklidge, J., & Tanner, R. (2001). Psychiatric, psychosocial, and cognitive functioning of Female adolescents with AD/HD. *Journal of the American Academy of Child and Adolescent Psychiatry, 40,* 530–540.

Safer, D. (2000). Are stiumulants overprescribed for youths with AD/HD? *Annals of Clinical Psychiatry, 12,* 55–62.

Safer, D.J., & Malever, M. (2000). Stimulant treatment in Maryland public schools. *Pediatrics, 106,* 533–539.

Surgeon General's Report, (2001). *Report of the surgeon general's conference on children's mental health: A national action agenda.* Department of Health and Human Services.

Teeter, P.A. (1998). *Interventions for AD/HD: Treatment in developmental context.* New York: Guilford Press.

Wolraich, M.L., Hannah, J.N., Pinnock, T.Y., Baumgaertel, A., & Brown, J. (1996). Comparison of diagnostic criteria for attention-deficit hyperactivity disorder in a county-wide sample. *Journal of American Academy of Child and Adolescent Psychiatry, 35,* 319–324.

Phyllis Anne Teeter Ellison, Ed.D., is the President of CHADD, 2005–07, and is a member of the *Attention!®* magazine Editorial Advisory Board.

This article first appeared in *Attention!®* magazine, June 2003.

A Gift to the CHADD Membership Support Fund Can Rescue a Family

*E*very year through the generosity of donors like you, CHADD is able to provide a limited number of annual memberships to applicants who cannot afford to join, but are in dire need of national and local CHADD services, information and support.

The Matt Cohen Membership Support Fund has been established to meet this ongoing demand. But the fund must be replenished each year.

Every tax-deductible donation of $45 will make a one-year membership possible.

Thank you in advance for your support.

CHADD is a nonprofit, tax-exempt IRS Section 501(c)(3) organization, and donations are tax deductible to the full extent of the law. (Matching donations by employers are welcome.)

CHADD®
CHILDREN AND ADULTS WITH
ATTENTION-DEFICIT/HYPERACTIVITY DISORDER

Here's my donation to the CHADD Membership Support Fund in the amount of:
❑ $45　　❑ $90　　❑ $135　　❑ $_____ Other

❑ Check (payable to CHADD)
❑ Visa　　❑ MC　　❑ Discover　　❑ American Express

_____　　_____
Name on Credit Card　　　　　　　　　　　　　Signature

_____　　_____
Credit Card No.　　　　　　　　　　　　　　　Expiration Date

_____
Name

_____
Street Address

_____
City　　　　　　　　　　　State　　　　　　Zip Code

Please return to: CHADD, Inc., Membership Support Fund
8181 Professional Place, Suite 150, Landover, MD 20785

Managing Social Skills All Day Every Day

By Harold S. Koplewicz, M.D.

Families affected by AD/HD are familiar with the many different ways the condition impacts the child and the entire family. Despite recognition of AD/HD as one of the most common mental health conditions among school-age children by leading authorities such as the American Psychiatric Association (APA), the American Academy of Pediatrics (AAP), and the American Academy of Child and Adolescent Psychiatry (AACAP), many people perceive AD/HD as just a "school-day disorder." While the effects of AD/HD on academics have been researched extensively, little has been done to examine its effect on social development of children.

The symptoms of AD/HD affect children morning, noon and night. A child with AD/HD is most often described as "the hyper one who constantly disrupts the class," but beyond academic difficulties, children with AD/HD have trouble managing social skills all day. They often find it difficult to follow rules and get along with family members, peers at school, those they encounter during after-school activities, and neighborhood children. A new survey helps shed light on parents' percep-tions of the all-day, every-day impact AD/HD has on all aspects of a child's life.

The national **I.M.P.A.C.T.** (**I**nvestigating the **M**indset of **P**arents about **AD/HD** & **C**hildren **T**oday) **2001 Survey** conducted by the New York University Child Study Center found that AD/HD takes a major toll on the life of a child and the whole family. Not sur-prising to anyone living in a household with a family member who has AD/HD, children

diagnosed with the disorder face serious social development issues that affect their relation-ships with family and friends. This is the first national study comparing the attitudes and perceptions of parents whose children have AD/HD with other parents whose children do not have the condition. The survey of more than 500 parents of children ages 6–14 was sponsored by an unrestricted educational grant from McNeil Consumer & Specialty Pharmaceuticals.

IMPACT at Home

Parents of children with AD/HD face more challenges in helping their child successfully complete everyday tasks. According to the sur-vey, they were more likely than other parents to report feeling frustrated while helping their child through daily activities, such as getting ready for school, doing homework and getting ready for bed. They also reported spending at least three hours a day helping their children with AD/HD manage their routines. Thirty-five percent of parents of children with AD/HD say they play "a major role" in their child's daily routine, compared to 23 percent of parents of children without AD/HD.

AD/HD also takes its toll on the relation-ships at home. Seventy-two percent of parents of children with AD/HD report that their child has trouble getting along with siblings or other family members, compared to 53 percent of parents of children without AD/HD. Parents often must devote extra time and energy to the child with AD/HD, leaving less time for other children. The family dynamics may focus on taking care of and meeting the needs of the child with AD/HD, but it's important for parents to carve out time for all of their children.

IMPACT at School: Beyond the 3 Rs

The school experience is much more than reading, writing and arithmetic. Peer relationships and a sense of belonging are important to a child's development. Many kids with AD/HD feel different just because they have been diagnosed with the condition. Add to this the label of "problem child" that can accompany the diagnosis, plus the stigma of taking medication during school, and it's easy to see why. As children get older, they may become uncomfortable when their peers question why they need to visit the nurse every day.

These feelings of not "fitting-in" are reflected in the survey results. Parents of children diagnosed with AD/HD are nearly three times more likely to report that their child has difficulty getting along with neighborhood children, more than twice as likely to say their child gets picked on, half as likely to believe their child has many good friends and are less likely to play with a group of friends than parents of children without AD/HD.

The IMPACT on After-School Activities

A majority of parents surveyed agree that participation in after-school activities, such as sports, clubs or after-school programs, is important to a child's emotional and social development. Sixty-nine percent of parents of children with AD/HD and 78 percent of parents of children without AD/HD report that their child participates in after-school activities. However, nearly one-quarter of parents of children with AD/HD say their child has problems that limit their participation in after-school activities, as compared to only seven percent of parents of children without AD/HD.

How can a child participate in after-school activities when he hardly gets by in school? Each day, children with AD/HD experience a series of clearly missed social cues. They don't pick up on social nuances, so the best type of weekend or after-school activities are important to help them practice learning social skills. The more success these children experience in different social settings, the better their self-esteem—that can make a huge difference in their lives. The right kind of activity can be invaluable to help redirect a child's energy, tap into hidden talents or interests and develop social skills. Games can often teach valuable life lessons and skills: concentration, anticipation and appreciation of others' strengths and weaknesses, the joy of victory and recovery from defeat.

> Peer relationships and a sense of belonging are important to a child's development.

The IMPACT of Not Treating AD/HD

Perhaps one of the more disturbing issues uncovered in the survey is that parents indicate many children are not following physician-recommended treatment for their condition. Research shows that left untreated, children with AD/HD can suffer academically and experience behavioral, social and emotional problems through adulthood.

Of parents of children with AD/HD, 45 percent say that behavior therapy has been recommended for their child, but less than one-quarter (21 percent) report that their child participates in behavior therapy. Additionally, 89 percent of parents of children with AD/HD report that their child has been prescribed medication to help manage the symptoms, but only 55 percent report their child is currently taking medication. While nearly all parents whose children take medication for their AD/HD report being concerned that their child gets the correct dosage of medication (99 percent) and is consistently medicated while at school (94 percent), far fewer are concerned about consistent medication during evenings and weekends (67 percent).

Parents should talk with their child's doctor about finding the right comprehensive treatment plan—one that may include behavioral modification, educational and social support, and medication, if appropriate. Recent treatment guidelines for AD/HD issued by the American Academy of Pediatrics state that, if appropriate, physicians should recommend behavior therapy and/or stimulant medication to improve specific symptoms in children with AD/HD. Today, longer-lasting, once-daily stimulant medications can help children with AD/HD effectively manage the symptoms of their condition before, during and after school, including weekends.

> Parents indicate many children are not following physician-recommended treatment for their condition.

AD/HD is not just a school-day disorder, it is an all-day disorder. Helping these children realize success means addressing all aspects of their daily lives. Maintaining a regular schedule, celebrating accomplishments, evaluating personal strengths and weaknesses, and building a support team of parents, teachers and coaches to work through challenges are just some ways to encourage the social development of a child with AD/HD. For more information about AD/HD and the I.M.P.A.C.T. survey, visit the NYU Child Study Center website: www.AboutOurKids.org.

Harold Koplewicz, M.D., is director of the NYU Child Study Center and a member of CHADD's Professional Advisory Board.

This article first appeared in *Attention!*® magazine, April 2002.

Guidelines for Pediatricians on AD/HD

The American Academy of Pediatrics recently published two sets of recommendations for diagnosing and treating AD/HD in school-aged children. The first, "Clinical Practice Guideline: Diagnosis and Evaluation of the Child with Attention-Deficit/Hyperactivity Disorder," provides recommendations for the assessment and diagnosis of children. It recommends that clinicians obtain evidence directly from parents or caregivers and classroom teachers about the symptoms of AD/HD. It also recommends assessment for co-existing conditions, such as learning disabilities.

The second, "Clinical Practice Guideline: Treatment of the School-Aged Child with Attention-Deficit/Hyperactivity Disorder," suggests that clinicians recommend medication and/or behavior therapy as appropriate to improve outcomes of children with AD/HD. In addition, it recommends that clinicians provide systematic follow-up for the child with AD/HD with information gathered from parents, teachers, and the child.

These guidelines, along with numerous features for parents on AD/HD, can be found at www.aap.org.

Assessing Complementary and Controversial Interventions: Tips for Parents

by Phyllis Anne Teeter Ellison, Ed.D.

In light of growing public interest in non-medication interventions for the treatment of AD/HD, CHADD's Professional Advisory Board (PAB) has updated CHADD's What We Know sheet on *Assessing Complementary and Controversial Interventions.* The revised sheet contains valuable information for understanding and evaluating complementary and controversial interventions in order to make informed decisions. This article summarizes some of the tips for parents that can be found in the fact sheet.

What to Ask Alternative Health Care Providers

♦ Have clinical trials been completed on this intervention? Do you have information summarizing these results? Clinical trials typically refer to controlled studies where an intervention is carefully evaluated under research conditions. Generally, clinical trials include the following characteristics: studies are repeated a number of times; participants are carefully screened before entering the study; participants are randomly assigned to a treatment; placebos or other interventions are included as a comparison to the new treatment; participants and researchers are not told which treatment is administered; and scientists have confidence in their findings. ***Providers should be prepared to answer these questions.*** As a parent, you may want to avoid these interventions if providers are unwilling or unable to answer these questions. Healthy skepticism is appropriate.

♦ Is public information about your alternative approach available from the National Center for Complementary and Alternative Medicine (NCCAM) at the National Institutes of Health (NIH)? You can contact NCCAM directly at (888) 644-6226 or visit its website at: www.nccam.nih.gov. NCCAM provides information about complementary and alternative medicines free of charge.

♦ Is there a national professional organization of practitioners? Do states require professional licensing and training requirements for practitioners who provide this treatment?

♦ Is this treatment reimbursed by health insurance? What out-of-pocket financial obligations will my family have? How long will this out-of-pocket financial obligation last?

What to Ask Yourself

The following questions may help you spot unproven treatments or therapies that promise more than they deliver.

♦ Is the treatment likely to work for you or your child? Does it claim to be a remedy for everyone with AD/HD and other health problems? Are case studies the only

medical community? If so, remember the old adage, "Buyer Beware!"

♦ How is it represented in the media? Does the researcher own the company marketing the treatment under study? What is the source of the information? Good sources include: universities, medical schools, government agencies (NIH and the National Institute of Mental Health), professional medical associations and national disorder/disease specific organizations (like CHADD). Professional affiliations and relevant credentials of "experts" should be provided. Reputable medical journals require that authors reveal possible conflicts of interest.

Tips for Negotiating the World Wide Web

Although the Internet is becoming a frequently used resource for medical information, it is also a low cost and global marketing place that is, at times, home to unreliable health information. Be sure to:

♦ Know where you are getting information from. Part of the web address will tell you about the source (e.g., .edu = university, .com = company, .org = non-profit organization, .gov = government agency).

♦ Obtain a second opinion regarding the information presented on the Web. Use part of a phrase or name and run it through a search engine to find other discussions on the topic. Finally, talk to your health care provider.

Don't forget to use the CHADD Web site at www.chadd.org. One of its major purposes is to provide information on evidenced-based treatments for AD/HD. The National Resource Center (NRC) on AD/HD is a CHADD program funded by the Centers for Disease

evidence presented for its efficacy? Is there only one study supporting its use? Do studies include a control group (i.e., a group that received no treatment)?

♦ How safe is the remedy? Does it include directions for proper use? Does it list the contents? Does it provide warnings of side effects? Most importantly, is it described as harmless or natural?

♦ How is the remedy promoted? Does it claim to have a secret formula? Does it claim to work immediately and permanently for everyone with AD/HD? Is it described as "astonishing," "miraculous" or an "amazing breakthrough?" Does it claim to cure AD/HD? Is it provided through only one source? Is it promoted through infomercials, self-promoting books or by mail order? Does it claim that it is being suppressed or unfairly attacked by the

Control and Prevention. The CHADD Web site provides a link to the NRC where you can access information on topics such as About AD/HD, Diagnosing and Treating AD/HD, Dealing with Systems, Educational Issues and Living with AD/HD. The NRC also has information in Spanish.

The latest revision of the complementary and controversial interventions sheet provides information on alternative, complementary and controversial treatments for AD/HD including dietary interventions (e.g., food eliminations), nutritional supplements, interactive metronome training, sensory integration therapy, anti-motion sickness medication, candida yeast, EEG biofeedback, chiropractic services, including applied kinesiology (realignment of bones in the skull), optometric vision training, thyroid treatment and lead treatment.

Finally, it is important that families consult with their physicians before using these interventions. A good medical history and physical examination are important to identify thyroid dysfunction, allergies, food intolerances, dietary imbalances or deficiencies, and other medical conditions that may mimic symptoms of AD/HD or affect or interact with treatments.

"Each child and each individual is unique. While multimodal treatment is the gold standard of treatment for AD/HD, not all individuals can tolerate medications, and medications are not always effective. Some individuals experience side effects that are too great. Being an informed consumer about the published

> It is important that families consult with their physicians before using these interventions.

science behind an intervention and frequently communicating with your medical doctor are important factors in determining if the interventions identified in this paper should be considered."[1]

Our thanks are extended to the CHADD Professional Advisory Board for their expertise and hard work on crafting these tips. You can access the revised sheet at the National Resource Center on AD/HD Web site, www.help4adhd.org/en/about.

Phyllis Anne Teeter Ellison, Ed.D., is the President of CHADD 2005–07, and is a member of the *Attention!*® magazine Editorial Advisory Board.

This article first appeared in *Attention!*® magazine, December 2003.

Medication Treatment within the Multimodal Context

by Mary Durheim

Providing a comprehensive and user-friendly review of medication for the treatment of attention-deficit/hyperactivity disorder (AD/HD) is a difficult task.

In December 1999, the National Institute of Mental Health (NIMH) set the gold standard of science-based treatment of AD/HD in its Multimodal Treatment Study of Children with AD/HD (MTA). CHADD's Professional Advisory Board currently defines multimodal treatment for children and adolescents with AD/HD as a combination of parent and child education about diagnosis and treatment, behavior management techniques, medication, and school programming and supports. Treatment should be tailored to the unique needs of each child and family.

Every family has to reach an informed decision about whether medication should be tried as part of a multimodal approach to treatment. Each of us arrives at this decision at different points in life. Some of us never reach this decision.

Clarke Ross, our CEO, and I have each used multimodal treatment—that is, behavioral interventions and medication—for our family members. We each were initially reluctant to use medication and first tried other alternatives. We hoped that we would not need medication for our family members, but each of us reached the point where we found medication therapeutically helpful.

In my family, our physician first suggested medication for our son Jay before he reached third grade. Reluctant to move in this direction, we instead tried a food-elimination diet, then counseling and then an array of other interventions. These alternative approaches did not work. After trying several other interventions, which also were unsuccessful, we decided to try medication. Jay was in the second semester of third grade.

Today, he is 27, successful, and still needs medication to keep his thoughts organized and to manage the many details that are part of his job. Despite a lot of trial and error, once we found the right treatment combination for Jay, the difference was like night and day. My daughter Jennifer and my husband Mike also take medication to deal with symptoms of AD/HD. To hear my daughter describe the difference this treatment approach has made is amazing, "I am able to think clearly and not have so much jumbled up in my head!" Both

For More Information...

Like all health issues, you must consider the risks versus benefits before making key decisions about whether to take medication. Talk with your doctor, and never be afraid to ask questions. For more information, we encourage you to use the National Resource Center on AD/HD Web site (www.help4adhd.org/en/about), where you can access information on AD/HD in children, adolescents and adults through the "What We Know" series.

of my children are extremely bright—they just couldn't always show what they knew.

Clarke's son Andrew is now 14. When Andrew was four, a child and adolescent psychiatrist recommended stimulant medication for his inattentive AD/HD. At the time, the Rosses were not convinced that AD/HD played a role in his delayed performance, and because of his history of febrile seizures, they declined medication. Andrew was enrolled in a special education preschool for children with language delays, and he received private sensory integration therapy to address his motor delays and tactile defensiveness. While helpful, these interventions did not seem to address his obvious impairments. By the time Andrew was 7, the Rosses were ready to try medication. The first two had little impact on Andrew's condition. The third medication worked well but resulted in a significant loss of appetite at lunch. To work around this, he has a large breakfast and has a healthy snack when he gets home from school. Behavioral management and multimodal treatment have been keys to his success in dealing with inattention and significant anxiety.

Every family's situation and experience is different. With your physician, be sure to rule out other possible medical conditions that might resemble the symptoms of AD/HD. It is equally important to understand that medications don't work for everyone and that most medications have side effects that range from mild to severe.

We wish you much success as you seek and identify appropriate treatments for your family members' disorders, including AD/HD.

Mary Durheim is the immediate past president of CHADD, 2003–05.

This article first appeared in *Attention!*® magazine, April 2005.

Start a CHADD Support Group in Your Community

Managing AD/HD every day is a challenge for any family or adult with AD/HD. Coming together with others who are facing the same challenges can be an enormous benefit for all who participate. If you are interested in starting a parent or adult support group in your community, contact the Chapter Services Department at CHADD at (301) 306-7070 ext 121 or go online to www.chadd.org\supportgroups. We will send you a Support Group Toolkit with everything you need to get started.

Managing AD/HD Anger

by Michael Romaniuk, Ph.D., and Cristen Marek

Having a quick temper or excessive anger can be a problem for anyone. Many people have trouble with angry outbursts, which impact their lives in a negative way. This problem can be even worse for adults with AD/HD, as many are emotionally oversensitive and overreactive to stimulation, making them more vulnerable to their surrounding environments. They may become easily irritated, annoyed or frustrated, anxious or worried, sad or depressed, or upset by teasing, criticism, rejection or disappointment. These adults are often easily provoked—just a little disruption can set them off, resulting in an angry response that is disproportionately severe or intense for the situation at hand. When being too quick to anger is a chronic problem, serious consequences for both the sender and receiver often result.

> The way you express anger can be improved, and the reasons for doing so are numerous.

An inability to keep anger in check has many far-reaching effects. It impacts all relationships—personal, professional and social. Uncontrolled anger may also limit success in your career and adversely affect your role as a spouse or parent. It can contribute to interpersonal conflicts, social isolation and feelings of low self-worth.

The problem is not in the emotion itself (it's okay to feel angry), but in the *expression* of it (huge outbursts are not acceptable). Fortunately, the way you express anger can be improved, and the reasons for doing so are numerous.

Negative Effects on Others

Inappropriate displays of anger can hurt many people. First, your own anger may be displaced. For example, because you can't yell at your boss when he or she does something to make you angry (which might result in your being fired), you might instead take your anger home and dump it on your spouse.

Second, your anger may affect another's health. Being on the receiving end of someone's misplaced anger is very stressful and can trigger a variety of physiological effects such as headaches, ulcers and hypertension. The person could become overwhelmed or unable to think, or shut down emotionally in order to avoid being overwhelmed by the emotions that the anger creates. They can also become depressed and withdraw from those around them to avoid getting hurt again.

This can result in feelings of insecurity, anxiety and vulnerability. They also may blame themselves for having provoked the anger asking, "What did I do wrong to deserve this?" Overall, those on the receiving end of an inappropriate outpouring of anger may feel hurt and unloved. When people are treated in this manner they often feel that they don't matter.

In addition to these negative feelings, the recipients of your anger could begin to distrust you and others in general. Even worse, they could retaliate with their own anger and perpetuate this vicious cycle.

How Anger Hurts You

Your own anger can also take a toll on you. Anger is aversive and can drive people away. Who wants to be around someone who is always losing his or her temper? It can destroy intimacy with others and tarnish your reputation, which could lead to guilty feelings about hurting others and could be embarrassing for you.

Anger can also hurt your mental functioning, leading to distortion, misperception and misinterpretation of reality. In the heat of anger, good judgment doesn't typically occur. And do you remember those headaches, ulcers and hypertension that your friends may have suffered from? Well, you can be affected by them too.

What Purpose Does Anger Serve?

You may be wondering, "Why do we even have anger? What is its purpose?" As noted earlier, anger is not always a bad thing. In some ways it can be helpful and adaptive. Consider one of anger's main purposes: protecting ourselves from imminent bodily harm. This aspect of anger is an innate, biological reflex that automatically occurs when faced with danger. Think of the "fight or flight" reflex when you encounter a threat. In this case you want to become as intimidating as possible to protect yourself. In instances where your own or another's safety is jeopardized, it is understandable and acceptable to feel and express your anger. Your life depends on it.

However, anger is also inappropriately used for non-life-threatening purposes such as influencing or controlling others. Consider the example of a major league baseball manager. At times you'll see the skipper fly onto the field screaming with his arms flailing and kicking dirt. He'll argue a call with the umpire by throwing a temper tantrum. He could be using anger to influence the umpire into changing his call or to prompt his team into joining him in ranting.

Anger can also be used as a means of conveying a direct and powerful message to others that you are upset, dislike something or want attention. If you give someone an angry look, you are using nonverbal means to tell the person that you are not happy with what he or she just did or said. Your angry demeanor sends the message.

When we use anger in these ways—to influence or communicate—we have learned to do so from those around us. Our families and society often have unspoken guidelines about which emotions can be shared and how they can be expressed. For instance, boys are often taught not to cry when they're hurt, but told it is okay to display anger in the same situation. For young girls, the opposite is more likely to be true. But as we have seen, the negative impact of displaying inappropriate anger is far too severe to make it worthwhile. Luckily, because how we display anger is *learned,* inappropriate expression can be *un*learned. More effective techniques to influence, control and communicate can replace anger, achieving the same results and eliminating the drawbacks.

> The first step in controlling your anger is to recognize and own your feelings.

How You Can Manage Your Anger

The first step in controlling your anger is to recognize and own your feelings. Don't blame others or deny that you have a problem. You have the power to change your behavior. Try to sensitize yourself to the negative effects of anger on others and on yourself, and work toward minimizing its display. Here are three strategies to help you do just that:

1. Say vs. Display

Don't *show* that you're angry, say it. Remember, it's the display of anger (e.g., yelling) that is destructive. Say that you're angry in a neutral tone. This way, others won't be put off by *how* you are saying something, and will be more likely to listen to *what* you're saying. You won't generate the negative effects of displaying your anger, but you can still influence and communicate in a more constructive manner. (And, when you become effective in saying how you feel and getting what you want, the angry feelings actually go away!)

2. Express your "true" emotion

Anger may not be the real emotion you are feeling—it could just be the easiest one to access and express. Some may have a limited emotional vocabulary because they were not taught or allowed to show a wide range of feelings. Some may have gotten the "don't be a crybaby" line, and others may not have learned to differentiate between emotions such as frustration, disappointment, hurt and anger. In reality, the range of emotions is wide. Think of the anger that may come with a divorce or the end of a relationship. A virtual laundry list of emotions could be hiding under that anger: feeling hurt, rejected, alone, hopeless, betrayed, vulnerable, misunderstood, frustrated or disrespected.

If anger is repeatedly felt and displayed without any relief, it may mean that anger is not the "true" emotion you are feeling, just the easiest for you to show. Therefore, you need to accurately identify your "true" underlying feeling. When this is done and "processed" or communicated, the anger goes away.

3. Develop realistic expectations

Sometimes anger results when expectations are not met, such as when others' behavior or our own falls short of what we expect. We may be surprised or disappointed, and view the accompanying anger as justified.

Take the example of road rage. Typically, another driver does something he or she shouldn't. In turn, you feel your anger is justified because you expected the driver to drive properly and obey the law. You may feel it is okay to express your anger because the driver's behavior fell short of your expectations. This makes your angry outburst the other driver's fault, not yours. However, another way of looking at this situation is that your expectations ("all drivers should obey the law") are unrealistic and you may be unintentionally setting yourself up for an angry response. Realistically speaking, it is unreasonable to believe bad driving will never occur. If we hold on to this belief, we set ourselves up for anger. But by adjusting lofty or perfectionist standards ("bad driving will happen sooner or later"), we are less likely to be surprised or disappointed, and anger is less likely to emerge.

To summarize, we have highlighted three strategies to help manage anger: saying versus displaying anger, finding and expressing your "true" emotion, and adjusting your expectations to meet reality. It is important to learn these techniques and to avoid inappropriate displays of anger given their detrimental effects. Not only can excessive or inappropriate anger hurt you and destroy your relationships, it will adversely affect those around you. The negative outcomes of anger far outweigh the positives. Because adults with AD/HD can react quickly, impulsively and inappropriately, learning these skills is even more important to maintaining relationships.

Michael Romaniuk, Ph.D., is coordinator of special programs in the Department of Psychiatry and Behavioral Sciences at Akron General Medical Center. He leads the adult AD/HD support group and can be reached at www.akrongeneral.org/add.

Cristen Marek is a freelance writer affiliated with Canisius College and a summer research fellow at Akron General Medical Center.

This article first appeared in *Attention!*® magazine, October 2003.

Chapter 3

AD/HD in Children

Managing Medicine for Children and Teenagers with AD/HD

Children or teens with attention-deficit/hyperactivity disorder (AD/HD) often have more problems than other people with paying attention, being hyperactive, or being impulsive (doing things rashly or suddenly, without thinking first). These problems may last throughout their lives.

If AD/HD is not diagnosed and treated early, it may lead to failing in school or dropping out. The symptoms might also lead to not doing well in a job, depression, and serious behavior problems. AD/HD can also cause children and adolescents problems with relationships, not living up to their ability, substance abuse, or serious antisocial or even criminal behavior.

About 3 percent to 7 percent of children—boys and girls—have AD/HD. Research shows AD/HD tends to run in families.

AD/HD is not caused by bad parenting, or by other factors in the child's home or family life.

> The child, the family, and the medical professional should work together to decide on a treatment plan.

Diagnosis of AD/HD

There is no single test to diagnose AD/HD. Anxiety, depression, and some learning disabilities are conditions that may seem like AD/HD. Health professionals (for example, pediatricians, psychologists or psychiatrists) must find out if the child has any of these conditions instead of or along with AD/HD.

To diagnose AD/HD, a health professional needs to know how the child or teenager is doing both at home and in school, socially as well as emotionally. The healthcare provider will ask questions of parents, teachers, and, of course, the child.

A physical exam by a medical professional should include hearing and vision checkups. This exam is also done to rule out other medical problems with symptoms that seem like AD/HD, but are not.

Treatment for AD/HD

Properly treating children and teens with AD/HD includes medical, educational and behavioral treatments. The term for this combination of treatments is *multimodal* treatment.

Part of the treatment is teaching the parents and the child about AD/HD. Parents will learn how to manage the child's behavior, about medications and other therapies, and how to get the school programs the child needs.

Treatment should be based on the unique needs of each child and family. Multimodal treatment is usually thought to be the best treatment plan.

The Role of Medication

For most children and teens, the medication prescribed by a doctor is an important part of AD/HD treatment. Medications are not used to control behavior. Instead, they are used to make the symptoms of AD/HD better.

Starting Medication

The child, the family, and the medical professional should work together to decide on a treatment plan. If medication is used, the doctor prescribes it. If the first medication is not helpful or has unacceptable side effects, the doctor will probably change the dose or try another medication.

Stimulant Medications

Stimulant medications are medications that stimulate the frontal parts of the brain that are not filtering out distractions as well as they should. The three most common types of stimulants used to treat AD/HD are methylphenidate (brand names: Concerta and Ritalin) amphetamine (brand name: Adderall) and dextroamphetamine (brand name: Dexadrine).

Between 70 percent and 80 percent of children with AD/HD do well with these medications. Their symptoms lessen. But the right medication and the right dose must be found for each individual.

Nonstimulant Medications

Some people do just as well or better by taking medications that are not stimulants. Nonstimulants are often used when people do not do well on stimulants.

A new medication (called Strattera) is specifically for AD/HD. It is not a stimulant, but it also helps with inattention and with hyperactive and impulsive symptoms of AD/HD.

Antidepressant medications are sometimes used for AD/HD, but not as often, to help with hyperactivity, anxiety or serious sleeping problems. Common antidepressants are Prozac, Zoloft, and Celexa.

Possible Side Effects of Medications for AD/HD

Most of the side effects when first using AD/HD medications are mild and may not last long. The most common side effects of stimulants are loss of appetite, headache, stomachache, and sleeping problems. The doctor usually can help manage these side effects. Strattera may lead in rare cases to severe liver injury resulting in liver failure if not stopped immediately on finding any liver effects (itching, dark urine, jaundice, right upper quadrant tenderness or unexplained "flu-like" symptoms).

Frequently Asked Questions

Q. How long does it take to find the right individual dose of medication?

A. The effects of a stimulant medication usually can be seen in 30 to 60 minutes, but finding the right dose and schedule for taking it may take a few weeks. Non-stimulant medications often need several weeks before they fully work.

Q. As my child grows, will the dosage need to be changed?

A. Not necessarily. Many teens and adults continue to do well on the same doses of stimulant medication. But others may need a higher dose.

Q. Will my child need to take medication forever, even into adulthood?

Many studies have shown that children and teens with AD/HD **not** treated with stimulant medications can have a higher risk of abusing illegal drugs.

A. These medications can be stopped at any time. AD/HD is an ongoing (or chronic) condition. However, about one-third of people who have AD/HD as children seem to outgrow the symptoms. People will have different long-term experiences and may find they need to take medication into adulthood.

Q. *Should medication be taken only when my child is in school?*

A. Talk to your doctor about this. Medication taken outside of school can help children get along with friends, avoid symptoms when at home, and pay attention while doing homework or at activities like sports.

Q. *Are children who take stimulant medications more likely to have substance abuse problems later in life?*

A. No. Many studies of children with AD/HD have found that using stimulant medications under a doctor's care does not increase the risk of later substance abuse. In fact, many studies have shown that children and teens with AD/HD **not** treated with stimulant medications can have a higher risk of abusing illegal drugs.

More Information

If you would like detailed information about the many medications used to treat AD/HD, CHADD will send you a fact sheet with details about each, or you can visit the NRC Web site at www.help4adhd.org.

The information in this article first appeared in the What We Know sheet, "Managing Medicine for Children and Teenagers with AD/HD," 2004. The sheet was supported by Cooperative Agreement No. R04/CCR321831-01 from the Centers for Disease Control and Prevention (CDC). The contents are solely the responsibility of the authors and do not necessarily represent the official views of CDC.

Behavioral Treatment for Children and Teenagers with AD/HD

Behavior treatment involves both social and psychological therapies. It is a very important part of treatment for attention-deficit/hyperactivity disorder (AD/HD) in children and teens.

Behavior modification or behavior therapy is also called psychosocial treatment. It works by changing the behavior of a child or adolescent. Research shows that behavioral treatments work well for the symptoms of AD/HD, especially when they are used with stimulant medication.

Treating AD/HD in children often involves medical, educational, and behavioral treatments used together. Treatment should be planned and carried out only after learning what individual needs each child and family have.

Why use behavioral treatments?

Behavioral treatment for AD/HD is important because it helps with issues such as:

♦ problems doing well in school
♦ behavior problems at school
♦ problems with friendships with others their age
♦ problems getting along with parents and with brothers and sisters

Behavioral treatments work by teaching new skills to parents, teachers and the children for handling problems.

What is behavior modification?

With behavior modification (or behavior therapy), parents, teachers and the child with AD/HD learn new skills for interacting with others. Adults teach the child or adolescent new ways of behaving by changing the ways

they themselves respond to the child's or teen's behaviors.

Parents and teachers should both use the new skills at the same time to get the best results. They should all do the following:

♦ Start with goals that the child can succeed at, in small steps.
♦ Be consistent—even at different times of the day, in different places and with different people around.
♦ Use the new skills over the long haul—not just for a few months.
♦ Remember that teaching and learning new skills take time, and the child's improvement will be little by little.

How does a behavior modification program begin?

The health professional begins by taking a complete history of the child's problems at home and school and during social activities. Most of this information comes from parents and teachers. The therapist also meets with the child to get a sense of what the child is like.

This evaluation should end with a list of *target behaviors* for treatment. Target behaviors are ones that need to be changed so the child gets better. They can be either behaviors that need to stop or new skills that need to be learned.

The areas targeted for treatment may not be the symptoms of AD/HD (such as being much too active, not paying attention, and doing rash or sudden things without thinking). Instead, they may address the problems that those symptoms cause in daily life, such as playing well with brothers and sisters, or obeying parent's requests.

Similar behavioral treatments are used both at home and at school. Parents and teachers carefully watch the child's response to the treatment. The treatment changes as the child changes.

Parent Training

Parents need careful teaching and support to learn the new parenting skills and how to use them all the time. The topics covered in parent-training sessions may include the following:

- ♦ Setting house rules and a routine
- ♦ Learning to praise wanted behaviors and to ignore mild unwanted behaviors (choosing your battles)
- ♦ Using appropriate ways to let the child know what you want from him or her

- ♦ Using "when…then" directions (when there is unwanted behavior, then adults take away rewards or privileges)
- ♦ Planning ahead and working with children in public places
- ♦ Using "time outs" during or after unwanted behavior
- ♦ Using daily charts and point systems for both rewards and consequences
- ♦ Using a school-home note system to reward school behavior and to track homework

Parent training can be done in groups with or without the child. Parent training can also happen during individual family sessions that include the child. When the child is a teenager, parent training is a bit different. Parents learn skills that are right for teens. The parents and

Parent to Parent is an intensive seven session training program for families on every aspect of treating, educating and supporting a child or adult with AD/HD. Classes are offered in local communities throughout the country. To find a class or a Certified Parent to Parent teacher near you, go to www.chadd.org/parent2parent.

teenager may meet with the therapist to come up with solutions they can agree on for behavioral problems. Parents try to gain improvements in the teenager's target behaviors (such as better grades in school) in exchange for rewards that they can control (such as allowing the teenager to go out with friends).

Therapy at School

Many children with AD/HD have teachers who may not know much about AD/HD or behavior modification. Parents of children with AD/HD should work closely with teachers to help them learn needed skills to manage behavior in classrooms.

Managing teenagers with AD/HD in school is different from managing children with AD/HD. Parents will often work with guidance counselors or other school staff rather than the individual teachers who will carry out the classroom behavior modification programs.

Therapy with the Child

Very often children with AD/HD have serious problems getting along with other children. Children who overcome these problems do better in the long run than those who don't.

Here are five good ways to help children who don't get along well with other children:

1. Teach social skills (how to get along with other people)
2. Help to solve social problems
3. Teach other skills that children find important, such as sports skills and board-game rules
4. Decrease unwanted behaviors such as bossiness or not sharing
5. Help to form a close friendship between the child with AD/HD and another child

To best help the child, the skills for changing unwanted behavior should be the same for the parent, school, and healthcare professional. The same behaviors should be watched, discouraged or encouraged, and rewarded in all three settings.

Social skills training groups are a common type of treatment. Social skills groups with children with AD/HD only work well when they are matched with what the parents and school are doing to reduce disruptive and negative behaviors.

What about combining behavior approaches with medication?

Both medication and behavioral treatment work well to improve AD/HD symptoms. Medication alone is more effective in treating AD/HD symptoms than behavioral treatment alone. In some cases, combining the two approaches works best. No one treatment plan is right for everyone.

The information in this article first appeared in the What We Know sheet, "Behavioral Treatment for Children and Teenagers with AD/HD," 2004. The sheet was supported by Cooperative Agreement No. R04/CCR321831-01 from the Centers for Disease Control and Prevention (CDC). The contents are solely the responsibility of the authors and do not necessarily represent the official views of CDC.

Parenting a Child with AD/HD

Often, when a child is diagnosed with AD/HD, the first response from his or her concerned parent is, "What can *I do* about it?" Although life with your child may at times seem challenging, it is important to remember that children with AD/HD can and do succeed. As a parent, you can help create home and school environments that improve your child's chances for success. The earlier you address your child's problems, the more likely you will be able to prevent school and social failure and associated problems such as underachievement and poor self-esteem that may lead to delinquency or drug and alcohol abuse.

Early intervention holds the key to positive outcomes for your child. Here are some ways to get started:

♦ **Don't waste limited emotional energy on self-blame.** AD/HD is the result of dysfunction in certain areas of the brain and in the majority of cases is inherited. It is not caused by poor parenting or a chaotic home environment, although the home environment can make the symptoms of AD/HD worse.

Multimodal treatment for children and adolescents with AD/HD consists of:

♦ Parent and child education about diagnosis and treatment;

♦ Behavior management techniques;

♦ Medication; and

♦ School programming and supports.

Treatment should be tailored to the unique needs of each child and family.

♦ **Learn all you can about AD/HD.** There is a great deal of information available on the diagnosis and treatment of AD/HD. It is up to you to act as a good consumer and learn to distinguish the "accurate" information from the "inaccurate." But how can you sort out what will be useful and what will not? In general, it is good to be wary about ads claiming to cure AD/HD. Currently, there is no cure for AD/HD, but you can take positive steps to decrease its impact.

♦ **Make sure your child has a comprehensive assessment.** To complete the diagnostic process, make sure your child has a comprehensive assessment that includes medical, educational, and psychological evaluations and that other disorders that either mimic or commonly occur with AD/HD have been considered and ruled out.

How to Ensure Your Child's Success at School

♦ **Become an effective case manager.** Keep a record of all information about your child. This includes copies of all evaluations and documents from any meetings concerning your child. You might also include information about AD/HD, a record of your child's prior treatments and placements, and contact information for the professionals who have worked with your child.

♦ **Take an active role in forming a team that understands AD/HD and wants to help your child.** Meetings at your child's school should be attended by the principal's designee, as well as a special educator and a classroom teacher that knows your child. You, however, have the right to request input at these meetings from others that understand AD/HD or your child's special needs. These include your child's physician, the school psychologist, and the nurse or guidance counselor from your child's school. If you have consulted other professionals, such as a psychiatrist, educational advocate or behavior management specialist, the useful information they have provided should also be made available at these meetings. A thorough understanding of your child's strengths and weaknesses and how AD/HD affects him will help you and members of this team go on to develop an appropriate and effective program that takes into account his or her AD/HD.

♦ **Learn all you can about AD/HD and your child's educational rights.** The more knowledge you have about your child's rights under the two education laws - the Individuals with Disabilities Education Act (IDEA) and Section 504 of the Rehabilitation Act - the better the chance that you will maximize his or her success. Each state has a parent training and information center that can help you learn more about your child's rights (visit www.taalliance.org/centers to find the center in your state).

♦ **Become your child's best advocate.** You may have to represent or protect your child's best interest in school situations, both academic and behavioral. Become an active part of the team that determines what services and placements your child receives in an Individualized Education Plan (IEP) or Section 504 plan.

How to Make Life at Home Easier

♦ **Join a support group.** Parents will find additional information, as well as support, by attending local CHADD meetings

where available. You can find the nearest chapter to your home on http://www.chadd.org chapter locator.

♦ **Seek professional help.** Ask for help from professionals, particularly if you are feeling depressed, frustrated and exhausted. Helping yourself feel less stressed will benefit your child as well.

♦ **Work together to support your child.** It is important that all of the adults that care for your child (parents, grandparents, relatives, and babysitters) agree on how to approach or handle your child's problem behaviors. Working with a professional, if needed, can help you better understand how to work together to support your child.

> The more knowledge you have about your child's rights under the two education laws, the better the chance that you will maximize his or her success.

♦ **Learn the tools of successful behavior management.** Parent training will teach you strategies to change behaviors and improve your relationship with your child. Identify parent training classes in your community through your local parent information and resource center (http://www.federalresourcecenter.org/fr/TAGuide/welcome.htm) or parent training and information center (http://www.taalliance.org/centers).

♦ **Find out if you have AD/HD.** Since AD/HD is generally inherited, many parents of children with AD/HD often discover that they have AD/HD when their child is diagnosed. Parents with AD/HD may need the same types of evaluation and treatment that they seek for their children in order to function at their best. AD/HD in the parent may make the home more chaotic and affect parenting skills.

Parent training will help you learn to:

♦ **Focus on certain behaviors and provide clear, consistent expectations, directions and limits.** Children with AD/HD need to know exactly what others expect from them. They do not perform well in ambiguous situations that don't specify exactly what is expected and that require they read between the lines. Working with a professional can help you narrow the focus to a few specific behaviors and help you set limits, and consistently follow through.

♦ **Set up an effective discipline system.** Parents should learn proactive—not reactive—discipline methods that teach and reward appropriate behavior and respond to misbehavior with alternatives such as "time out" or loss of privileges.

♦ **Help your child learn from his or her mistakes.** At times, negative consequences will arise naturally out of a child's behavior. However, children with AD/HD have difficulty making the connection between their behaviors and these consequences. Parents can help their child with AD/HD make these connections and learn from his or her mistakes.

How to Boost Your Child's Confidence

♦ **Tell your child that you love and support him or her unconditionally.** There will be days when you may not believe this yourself. Those will be the days when it is even more important that you acknowledge the difficulties your child faces on a daily basis, and express your love. Let your child know that you will get through the smooth and rough times together.

♦ **Assist your child with social skills.** Children with AD/HD may be rejected by peers because of hyperactive, impulsive or aggressive behaviors. Parent training can help you learn how to assist your child in making friends and learning to work cooperatively with others.

♦ **Identify your child's strengths.** Many children with AD/HD have strengths in certain areas such as art, athletics, computers or mechanical ability. Build upon these strengths, so that your child will have a sense of pride and accomplishment. Make sure that your child has the opportunity to be successful while pursuing these activities and that his strengths are not undermined by untreated AD/HD. Also, avoid, as much as possible, targeting these activities as contingencies for good behavior or withholding them, as a form of punishment, when your child with AD/HD misbehaves.

♦ **Set aside a daily "special time" for your child.** Constant negative feedback can erode a child's self-esteem. A "special time," whether it's an outing, playing games, or just time spent in positive interaction, can help fortify your child against assaults to self-worth.

Suggested Reading

For Help Parenting Your Children and Teens

Barkley, Russell (2000). *Taking Charge of ADHD: The Complete Authoritative Guide for Parents* (Revised Edition). New York: Guilford Press.

Brooks, Robert and Goldstein, Sam (2001). *Raising Resilient Children: Fostering Strength, Hope, and Optimism in Your Child.* Lincolnwood, IL: Contemporary Books.

Copeland, Edna and Love, Valerie (1995). *Attention, Please! A Comprehensive Guide for Successfully Parenting Children with Attention Deficit Disorders and Hyperactivity.* Plantation, FL: Specialty Press.

Dishion, Thomas J. and Patterson, Scot G. (1996). *Preventive Parenting with Love, Encouragement, and Limits: The Preschool Years.* Eugene, OR: Castalia Publishing Co.

Edwards, C. Drew (1999). *How to Handle a Hard-To-Handle Kid: A Parents' Guide to Understanding and Changing Problem Behaviors.* Minneapolis, MN: Free Spirit Publishing.

Flick, Grad (1996). *Power Parenting for Children with ADD/ADHD: A Practical Parent's Guide for Managing Difficult Behaviors.* San Francisco, CA: Jossey-Bass.

Forgatch, Gerald R. and Forgatch, Marion S. (2005). *Parents and Adolescents Living Together, Part 1: The Basics.* Champaign, IL: Research Press.

Forgatch, Gerald R. and Forgatch, Marion S. (2005). *Parents and Adolescents Living Together: Part 2: Family Problem Solving.* Champaign, IL: Research Press.

Heininger, Janet E. and Weiss, Sharon (2001). *From Chaos to Calm: Effective Parenting of Challenging Children with ADHD and Other Behavioral Problems.* New York, NY: Perigee Books.

Monastra, Vincent (2004). *Parenting Children with ADHD: 10 Lessons That Medicine Cannot Teach.* Washington, DC: Magination press

Phelan, Thomas (2003). *1-2-3 Magic: Training your child to do what you want!* (Third Edition) Glen Ellyn, Illinois: ParentMagic Inc.

Parker, Harvey (1999). *The ADD Hyperactivity Workbook for Parents, Teachers, and Kids* (Third Edition) Plantation, FL: Specialty Press.

Silver, Larry (1999). *Dr. Larry Silver's Advice to Parents on ADHD* (Second Edition). New York, NY: Three Rivers Press.

For Help With Your Child's Social Skills

Cohen, Cathi (2000). *How to Raise Your Child's Social IQ: Stepping Stones to People Skills for Kids.* Washington, DC: Advantage Books.

Frankel, Fred (1996). *Good Friends Are Hard to Find: Helping Your Child Find, Make and Keep Friends.* Glendale, CA: Perspective Publishing.

Sheridan, Susan (1998). *Why Don't They Like Me? Helping Your Child Make and Keep Friends.* Longmont, CO: Sopris West.

For Help Navigating the Educational Maze

Anderson, Winifred; Chitwood, Stephen; and Hayden, Deidre (1997). *Negotiating the Special Education Maze: A Guide for Parents and Teachers* (3rd Edition). Bethesda, MD: Woodbine House.

Jensen, Peter S. (2004). *Making the System Work for Your Child with ADHD.* New York, NY: Guilford Press.

Latham, Peter; and Latham, Patricia (1997). *Attention Deficit Disorder and the Law* (Second Edition). Washington, D.C.: JKL Publications.

Weingartner, Paul L (1999). *ADHD Handbook for Families—A Guide to Communicating with Professionals.* Washington, DC: Child and Family Press.

> Many children with AD/HD have strengths in certain areas such as art, athletics, computers or mechanical ability. Build upon these strengths.

The information in this article first appeared in the What We Know sheet, "Parenting a Child with AD/HD," 2004. The sheet was supported by Cooperative Agreement No. R04/CCR321831-01 from the Centers for Disease Control and Prevention (CDC). The contents are solely the responsibility of the authors and do not necessarily represent the official views of CDC.

Five Components of Executive Function and How They Impact School Performance

By Chris A. Zeigler Dendy, M.S.

Parents and teachers are often baffled when students with AD/HD, including those who are intellectually gifted, teeter on the brink of school failure. Recently, researchers may have solved part of this challenging puzzle: deficits in critical cognitive skills, known as *executive function,* may interfere with a student's ability to succeed in school. Practically speaking, executive function deficits may cause problems for students with AD/HD in several important areas: getting started and finishing work, remembering homework, memorizing facts, writing essays or reports, working math problems, being on time, controlling emotions, completing long-term projects and planning for the future.

Although scientists have not yet agreed on the exact elements of executive function, two AD/HD researchers, Russell Barkley, Ph.D., and Tom Brown, Ph.D., have given us insightful working descriptions. Dr. Barkley describes executive function as those "actions we perform to ourselves and direct at ourselves so as to accomplish self-control, goal-directed behavior and the maximization of future outcomes." Through use of a metaphor, Dr. Brown gives us a helpful visual image by comparing executive function to the conductor's role in an orchestra. The conductor organizes various instruments to begin playing singularly or in combination, integrates the music by bringing in and fading certain actions, and controls the pace and intensity of the music.

Although the impact of executive function deficits on school success is profound, this fact is often unrecognized by many parents and teachers. I learned the hard way with my own son that a high IQ score alone was not enough to make good grades. Early in my son's academic career, I knew something was interfering with his ability to do well in school. But it wasn't until Dr. Barkley identified the central role executive function plays in school success, that I finally understood why school was so difficult for him.

Components of Executive Function

Based upon material from Barkley and Brown, I have outlined five general components of executive function that impact school performance:

- ♦ **Working memory and recall** (holding facts in mind while manipulating information; accessing facts stored in long-term memory).
- ♦ **Activation, arousal and effort** (getting started; paying attention; finishing work).
- ♦ **Emotion control** (ability to tolerate frustration; thinking before acting or speaking).
- ♦ **Internalizing language** (using "self-talk" to control one's behavior and direct future actions).
- ♦ **Complex problem solving** (taking an issue apart, analyzing the pieces, reconstituting and organizing it into new ideas).

Let's take a more in-depth look at the first element of executive function—deficits in working memory and recall—and their impact on schoolwork.

Poor Working Memory and Recall

Affects the here and now:
- ♦ limited working memory capacity
- ♦ weak short-term memory (holding information in mind for roughly 20 seconds; capacity—roughly the equivalent of seven numbers)
- ♦ forgetfulness—can't keep several things in mind

As a result, students:
- ♦ have difficulty remembering and following instructions
- ♦ have difficulty memorizing math facts, spelling words and dates
- ♦ have difficulty performing mental computation such as math in one's head
- ♦ forget one part of a problem while working on another segment
- ♦ have difficulty paraphrasing or summarizing

Affects their sense of past events:
- ♦ difficulty recalling the past

As a result, students:
- ♦ do not learn easily from past behavior (limited hindsight)
- ♦ repeat misbehavior

Affects their sense of time:
- ♦ difficulty holding events in mind
- ♦ difficulty using their sense of time to prepare for upcoming events and the future

As a result, students:
- ♦ have difficulty judging the passage of time accurately
- ♦ do not accurately estimate how much time it will take to finish a task; conse-

quently, they may not allow enough time to complete work

Affects their sense of self-awareness:
- ♦ diminished sense of self-awareness

As a result, students:
- ♦ do not easily examine or change their own behavior

Affects their sense of the future:
- ♦ students live in the present—focus on the here and now
- ♦ less likely to talk about time or plan for the future

As a result, students:
- ♦ have difficulty projecting lessons learned in the past, forward into the future (limited foresight)
- ♦ have difficulty preparing for the future

Common Academic Problems Linked to AD/HD and Executive Function Deficits

Many students with AD/HD have impaired working memory and slow processing speed, which are important elements of executive function. Not surprisingly, these skills are critical for writing essays and working math problems.

A recent research study by Mayes and Calhoun has identified written expression as the most common learning problem among students with AD/HD (65 percent). Consequently, writing essays, drafting book reports or answering questions on tests or homework is often very challenging for these students. For example, when writing essays, students often have difficulty holding ideas in mind, acting upon and

> Many students with AD/HD have impaired working memory and slow processing speed.

organizing ideas, quickly retrieving grammar, spelling and punctuation rules from long-term memory, manipulating all this information, remembering ideas to write down, organizing the material in a logical sequence, and then reviewing and correcting errors.

Since learning is relatively easy for most of us, sometimes we forget just how complex seemingly simple tasks such as memorizing multiplication tables or working a math problem really are. For example, when a student works on a math problem, he must fluidly move back and forth between analytical skills and several levels of memory (working, short-term and long-term memory). With word problems, he must hold several numbers and questions in mind while he decides how to work a problem. Next, he must delve into long-term memory to find the correct math rule to use for the problem. Then, he must hold important facts in mind while he applies the rules and shifts information back and forth between working and short-term memory to work the problem and determine the answer.

To further complicate matters, other serious conditions may co-occur with AD/HD. According to the recent landmark National Institute of Mental Health multimodal treatment study on AD/HD (1999), two-thirds of children with AD/HD have at least one other co-existing problem, such as depression or anxiety.

Accommodating students with complex cases of AD/HD is critical! These children are at greater risk than their peers for a multitude of school problems, for example, failing a grade, skipping school, suspension, expulsion and sometimes dropping out of school and not going to college.

> Succeeding in school is one of the most therapeutic things that can happen to a child!

Favorite School Success Strategies

Over the years, I have collected several favorite teaching strategies and accommodations that work well for students with AD/HD. Here are just a few of those tips:

General teaching strategies
♦ Make the learning process as concrete and visual as possible.

Written expression
♦ Dictate information to a "scribe" or to parents.
♦ Use graphic organizers to provide visual prompts.
♦ Use "post-it" notes to brainstorm essay ideas.

Math
♦ Use paired learning (teacher explains problem, students make up their own examples, swap problems and discuss answers).
♦ Use a peer tutor. (After barely passing high school and college algebra, my son made an A in calculus plus had a 100 average on tests when the professor used this strategy. At the same time, he also tutored a friend.)

Memory
♦ Use mnemonics (memory tricks), such as acronyms or acrostics, e.g., HOMES to remember names of the Great Lakes.
♦ Use visual posting of key information on strips of poster board.

Modify teaching methods
Use an overhead projector to demonstrate how to write an essay. (Parents may simply write on paper or a computer to model this skill.)
♦ Use color to highlight important information.
♦ Use graphic organizers to help students organize their thoughts.

Modify assignments—reduce written work
- ♦ Shorten assignments.
- ♦ Check time spent on homework, and reduce it if appropriate (when total homework takes longer than roughly 10 minutes per grade as recommended in a PTA/NEA Policy, e.g. 7th grader = 70 minutes).
- ♦ Write answers only, not the questions (photocopy questions).

Modify testing and grading
- ♦ Give extended time on tests.
- ♦ Divide long-term projects into segments with separate due dates and grades.
- ♦ Average two grades on essays—one for content and one for grammar.

Modify level of support and supervision
- ♦ Appoint a "row captain" to check that homework assignments are written down and later turned into the teacher.
- ♦ Increase the amount of supervision and monitoring for these students if they are struggling.

Use technology
- ♦ Use a computer as often as possible.
- ♦ Use software to help teach skills.

Unfortunately students with AD/HD are often punished for executive function deficits such as lack of organizational and memory skills that interfere with their ability to bring home the correct homework assignments and books. Hopefully, after reading this article, teachers and parents will develop more innovative intervention strategies. For example, one effective alternative would be to have someone (a friend or teacher aide), meet the student at his locker to get the necessary homework materials together. Ultimately, this process of "modeling" and "shaping" behavior at the critical "point of performance" will help the student master skills or at a minimum, teach him to compensate for deficits.

Clearly school is often very difficult for students with AD/HD. However, when executive function deficits are also present, the accompanying problems are often overwhelming to the student and family. Unfortunately, some parents and teachers have had little awareness or sympathy for the challenges presented by these combined deficits. Hopefully, teachers and parents now realize that AD/HD is often a very complex condition. It is much more than just a simple case of hyperactivity. When deficits in executive function and related learning problems are present, students can try their very best and still not succeed in school.

So what should parents and teachers do with this new information? Identify the student's specific learning problems (e.g., written expression or math) and their executive function deficits (e.g., working memory, disorganization, forgetfulness, or impaired sense of time) and provide accommodations in both areas.

I leave you with this food for thought, "Succeeding in school is one of the most therapeutic things that can happen to a child! So do whatever it takes to help the child succeed in school."

On a personal note, our youngest son struggled terribly throughout his school years with AD/HD and executive function issues. Although college was very difficult, he is a senior and will graduate this year. So, if your child is struggling in school, do not give up. My family offers living proof that there is hope and help for AD/HD and coexisting conditions.

References

Barkley, Russell A. (1998). *Attention Deficit Hyperactivity Disorder.* New York: The Guilford Press.

Brown, Thomas E. (2000). *Attention Deficit Disorders and Co-morbidities in Children, Adolescents, and Adults.* Washington, DC: American Psychiatric Press.

Dendy, Chris A. Zeigler *Teaching Teens with ADD and AD/HD*. Bethesda, MD: Woodbine House, 2000

Dendy, Chris A. Zeigler *Teenagers with ADD*. Bethesda, MD: Woodbine House, 1995.

Deschler, Donald D., Edwin S. Ellis, and B. Keith Lenz *Teaching Adolescents with Learning Disabilities*. Denver, CO: Love Publishing Company, 1996.

Levine, Mel *Educational Care*. Cambridge, MA: Educators Publishing Service, 1994.

Mayes Susan D. and Susan Calhoun "Prevalence and Degree of Attention and Learning Problems in AD/HD and LD." AD/HD Report, v. 8, n. 2, April 2000.

Chris A. Zeigler Dendy. M.S., has over 30 years experience as a teacher, school psychologist, mental health counselor and administrator. More importantly, she is the mother of two grown sons with AD/HD. Ms. Dendy is the author of two popular books on AD/HD and producer of two videotapes, Teen to Teen: the ADD Experience and Father to Father. She is also co-founder of Gwinnett County CHADD (Ga.) and a member of the CHADD Board of Directors.

This article first appeared in *Attention!*® magazine, February 2002.

Strategies to Promote Homework Completion and Accuracy

Homework Target	What can teachers do?	What can parents do?	What can students do?
Completion	• Assign a reasonable amount of homework • Establish rewards and consequences for completing homework • Break long-term projects into segments and establish due dates for each segment	• Schedule a regular time and location for homework • Break homework into segments and establish reasonable time limits for completion • Allow child to take a short break (1–2 min.) between segments and use a timer to track the amount of time until the break • Reward child for completion with a privilege	• Record complete assignment, due date and necessary materials in homework assignment book • Check with a reliable classmate to ensure that the necessary materials are taken home • Ask to have an extra set of textbooks to keep at home or bring home all textbooks every day
Accuracy	• Practice skills necessary to complete homework in class • Ensure that homework is recorded correctly and completely in student's assignment book • Provide written homework assignments (i.e., on the chalkboard or school Web site)	• Instruct child in the skills necessary to complete homework before s/he begins the assignment • Limit distractions during homework • Reward child for accuracy with a privilege	• Ask teacher or parent for help before beginning homework • Work carefully during homework • Check and double-check homework

Peer Problems

By Holly J. Zumpfe and Steven Landau

Frequently, children with attention-deficit/hyperactivity disorder (AD/HD) may present serious difficulties with attentional and behavioral control in a variety of settings. Consequently, they may have management problems at home and school, and are at elevated risk for achievement delays and learning disabilities. To make matters worse, some of these children also experience seriously disturbed peer relations. For example, some children with AD/HD reveal they have few (if any) friends, and play with those much younger than themselves. Sadly, our research indicates that some classmates may consider them aversive playmates and objectionable work partners in the classroom. Using sociometric methods of data collection, in which students are asked to nominate among classmates, "whom they like the most" and "whom they like the least" (or "dislike the most"), it has been shown, repeatedly, that many children with AD/HD are the most rejected among their classmates. In fact, some researchers have suggested the social problems of these children may be central to an understanding of their overall psychopathology.

For parents and educators, these social concerns must be taken seriously. Research in developmental psychology makes it clear that any child with peer problems may be deprived of a number of important learning experiences, including the principles of egalitarian interactions (i.e., to "give and take" with others). Additionally, the notion of social competence is central to all federal and state legal definitions of developmental disabilities in comparison with assessment of adaptive behavior. Thus, successful development and peer relations seem to overlap conceptually and behaviorally.

Second, children with peer problems may experience higher levels of loneliness and other emotional effects, including serious worry about their social problems. Obviously, being disliked can be extremely painful. Take the anecdote of a second grade boy, described by Putallez and Gottman (1983), revealing (with spelling errors intact) the suffering he experienced: "i can hide. i am a little boy. i don't have friends but i have som friends but win i wait at the busstop som people haet me and some like me…one day i was moving so people would not tesz me in ne more but again they tesz me" (p. 13).

Social stigmatization of this sort further diminishes self-esteem and subsequent opportunities for peer interactions. Thus, a vicious cycle emerges in which rejection leads to less chance to practice appropriate social behaviors, which then evokes greater exclusion.

Third, we know that rejected children (including those with AD/HD) are the recipients of teasing and other forms of peer victimization. Teasing can lead to explosive retaliatory

> Many children with AD/HD are the most rejected among their classmates.

behavior, especially from those with AD/HD, (e.g., fighting back) that exacerbates an already negative reputation.

Finally, research consistently documents that children's negative reputation or status—especially peer rejection—is extremely durable, recurrent and often escalating. Those who are disliked by classmates during the elementary years often experience rejection in high school and continue to have relationship problems throughout adulthood. Unfortunately, many parents of children with AD/HD do not have information about how their son or daughter is functioning in the social domain. Most peer problems occur at school, and most teachers tend to focus on disruptive classroom behavior and academic performance difficulties. Parent conferences at school should address, among other things, how well the child with AD/HD is getting along with others.

Do all children with AD/HD experience the same peer problems?

Even though there is limited research addressing this question, and findings are not consistent, children with different types of AD/HD may experience different problems in the social arena. Those who are hyperactive/impulsive and inattentive (i.e., AD/HD combined type) may be rejected or more disliked by peers than those whose primary problems involve inattention exclusively (i.e., AD/HD-predominantly inattentive type). Peer relations of children in the latter group may include solitary, disengaged and onlooking behavior, with lower levels of sustained social interactions. These children tend to be ignored and neglected. In contrast, those with AD/HD-combined type are more likely viewed as aversive playmates, and tend to be actively disliked. One explanation for this difference rests with the fact that children with AD/HD-combined type may be more socially disruptive; they may start fights and rely on hostile explanations or attributions to account for the behavior of others. In addition, they may be more likely to

present additional problems that further alienate them from peers. The most likely culprit is comorbid difficulties with aggression and conduct disorder, and evidence is clear that many forms of aggression (but not all) evoke peer rejection.

An important issue when considering these peer problems involves the distinction between a social skill vs. social performance deficit. As explained by Landau, Milich, and Deiner (1998), reconciling this difference can determine which intervention is suitable for the child. For example, children who have a **social skill deficit** have not mastered age-appropriate social behavior and do not know how to make and keep friends. They lack the ability to accurately read social cues and often use inappropriate communication in social exchanges. In contrast, those with a **social performance deficit** have these necessary skills or knowledge (i.e., they know how to behave appropriately), but are unable to apply their skills in everyday interactions with other children. In other words, their problems are best understood as an inability to "perform what they know."

To date, there is controversy regarding which hypothesis explains the peer problems of children with AD/HD. However, work in our lab supports the performance-deficit position, which is also consistent with Barkley's (1997) unifying theory of AD/HD. We should assume that children who present a social skill deficit would benefit from social skills training (SST) in which they learn age-appropriate social behavior, reading of social cues and social perspective taking. In contrast, those with a social performance deficit should be trained to develop control strategies (e.g., anger management training) so they can apply what they already know. This distinction has been lost in many intervention efforts. What does the treatment research suggest?

There is no doubt that psychostimulants (e.g., methylphenidate) are the most effective treatment to reduce socially aversive and disruptive behaviors in children with AD/HD.

Unfortunately, medication-related improvements will not make these children better liked (i.e., peer rejection remains relatively unaffected). There are several explanations for this disappointing fact. Once disliked, improved social behavior following medication tends to be discounted by peers who are already "turned off." Second, the short-acting effects of psychostimulants can leave the child in a non-medicated state during school periods when children most likely engage in unsupervised free-play (e.g., lunch and recess or when school is dismissed). Our research (Day & Landau, 2002) provides a potential third explanation: the child's medication status at school may be stigmatizing in itself, and this may further reveal to others the "unusualness" of a child with AD/HD. This stigma is then exacerbated when classmates witness, due to the short half-life of some medications, both improved and deteriorating behavior throughout the school day.

Because of the above, we must assume medication alone will not address the peer problems of children with AD/HD. However, while on medication, these children may be more responsive to psychosocial (i.e., non-pharmacological) interventions in school. These other programs, which include anger management, attribution retraining and behavior management in the classroom (especially response-cost and timeout) should be used in conjunction with medication (see Landau et al., 1998, for a review of relevant psychosocial or social skills training programs).

We offer the following suggestions:

♦ Parents should not assume their son or daughter is without peer problems simply because the teacher has not reported such.

♦ If a child with AD/HD is having peer problems, assume they may be chronic and require systematic intervention. Many social skills training (SST) packages were designed for 10–12 sessions and to be dispensed once per week. This is insufficient; an on-going intervention for the entire school year may be necessary.

♦ There are no known SST interventions designed explicitly for children with AD/HD. As such, the nature of peer difficulties of each child should be assessed, and a treatment selected based on the strengths and limitations of each child.

♦ Best evidence indicates SST programs should be delivered in small groups (i.e., 4–8 same gender classmates), not one-on-one. This will increase the chance for positive feedback from peers and successful transfer from the training group to the classroom. In addition, some of the more popular children should also be included in these groups. Their presence may reduce the stigma of participating and help their less popular peers interact more positively with the other students.

Medication alone will not address the peer problems of children with AD/HD.

♦ SST objectives should be infused in all classroom activities. For example, if the child with AD/HD is trained to self-monitor and keep a daily log of interpersonal conflicts, this should be done throughout the school day and prompted by the teacher when necessary. The trainer must communicate regularly with teachers so training objectives can be reinforced by all adults in school.

♦ Parents should be involved in these interventions through home/school collaboration. This will strengthen school-based success and aid transfer to social activities after school. The SST described by Sheridan, Dee, Morgan, McCormick, and Walker (1996) provides an excellent example of parent involvement.

If an individual assessment of social problems is conducted and an intervention is planned involving teachers and parents, and the child's unique characteristics (i.e., not relying on packaged programs), there is reason to remain hopeful that the disturbed peer relations of children with AD/HD can be addressed.

References

Barkley, R. A. (1997). Behavior inhibition, sustained attention, and executive functions: Constructing a unifying theory of AD/HD. *Psychological Bulletin, 121,* 65–94.

Day, J. & Landau, S. (2002). *The message of medication: Peer perceptions of persistence, treatment acceptability, and social acceptance of a boy with AD/HD.* Unpublished manuscript.

Landau, S., Milich, R., & Diener, M. B. (1998). Peer relations of children with attention-deficit hyperactivity disorder. *Reading and Writing Quarterly: Overcoming Learning Difficulties, 14,* 83–105.

Pfiffner, L. J., Calzada, E., & McBurnett, K. (2000). Interventions to enhance social competence. *Child and Adolescent Psychiatric Clinics of North America, 9,* 689–709.

Putallez, M. & Gottman, J. (1983). Social relationship problems in children: An approach to intervention. In B. Lahey and A. E. Kazdin (Eds.), *Advances in clinical child psychology* (pp. 1–43). New York: Plenum Press.

Sheridan, S. M., Dee , C. C., Morgan, J. C., McCormick, M. E., & Walker, D. (1996). A multi-method intervention for social skills deficits in children with AD/HD and their parents. *School Psychology Review, 25,* 57–76.

Holly J. Zumpfe, M.S., is presently a doctoral student in the APA-approved Ph.D. program in School Psychology at Illinois State University. Steven Landau is Professor, Department of Psychology, Illinois State University.

This article first appeared in *Attention!*® magazine, April 2002.

AD/HD through a Parent's Eyes

by Tammy Young

I'm not sure when I first began to question my sanity. I had known for some time that my life was unmanageable. It was clear that my children were the focal point of the chaos that had become my everyday experience. I had explored every avenue, read every book and talked to every professional available. I had attended doctor's appointments without end, therapy sessions without merit, lectures by non-believers, and had been subjected to countless hours of supermarket-generated advice. After all of that, I still knew only one thing: my children had attention-deficit/hyperactivity disorder.

As I continued to seek answers for my children and their AD/HD, I also began to seek answers for myself. How could I maintain a positive outlook on life when everything seemed to be spinning out of control? How could I build meaningful, nurturing relationships with my children when so much energy was being spent on their shortcomings? How could I deal with the issues inherent to this disorder and preserve my sanity?

These questions led me on a journey of discovery that changed my life. I gained an understanding of the disorder and the tools necessary to manage it. More importantly, I changed the way I look at my children and their adversities, and the way I define my role as a parent.

Because AD/HD looks different in each individual, an understanding of the disorder itself is crucial to our ability to accept our children as they are without being overly critical of their mistakes. We must be able to differentiate between choice and ability in order to assist our children in overcoming the obstacles they face. It is this awareness that enables us to identify the most effective behavior management strategies for our children.

As we seek answers for ourselves and our children, it is easy to become overwhelmed by the sheer volume of information. Obtaining a diagnosis can be a difficult process in and of itself. Then there are difficult decisions to be made about treatment options. There are literally hundreds of books offering a variety of views and conflicting advice on diagnosis, treatment, management and educational issues. It takes time to muddle through the various techniques and strategies to find an approach that will work for each of us. Not only does an approach have to seem logical, it must also be something we know we can commit to and use consistently.

Raising a child with AD/HD may require us to evaluate the ways in which we discipline, and even our ideas about discipline in general. Discipline is teaching a child how to behave acceptably and to be accountable for his or her own actions. It is a process of molding and shaping as opposed to bending and breaking. We must develop a personalized approach for what ultimately will be a work in progress.

As a parent, my responsibility is to protect my children and guide them in their development. While they may be resistant to my guidance at times, I need to remember that I won't always be able to determine when and how they will learn important lessons. No matter how badly I want to share my wisdom with them, I cannot make them hear. Sometimes the greatest lessons are those learned the hard way.

Many of their lessons will come from family interactions. Meaningful lessons about relationships, responsibility and fairness evolve through family dynamics. What kind of problem-solvers will they become? How will they deal with the mistakes of others? Will they be able to accept responsibility for their actions?

Ultimately, I set the climate—my attitude, actions and willingness to laugh establish the tone for my children. It is my job to create an environment of love and compassion. We cannot afford to allow our fear, frustration and disappointment to be the driving forces in how we manage this disorder. We must be accepting of ourselves and practice patience and forgiveness as we learn a new way of thinking and being with our children.

> We cannot afford to allow our fear, frustration and disappointment to be the driving forces in how we manage this disorder.

My own transformation came when I realized I was the one who needed to change. In order to be an effective parent, I would have to identify those things within me that got in the way. I had to shift the focus from my children's challenges to my own. After all, how can we ask a child to change if we don't have the courage to change ourselves?

Acquiring a new perspective is not always an easy task, but it is well worth the effort. The changes we make on the inside lead to amazing changes on the outside. As we alter the ways in which we relate and respond to our children, they begin to respond differently as well.

We can accept our children as they are and develop an appreciation and respect for the challenges they face. We all have things to overcome. Our challenges are very personal. Our children are here with their own unique challenges, which are critical to their personal journeys. We must release our desire to free them from those challenges along with the notion that we can somehow change them into someone they are not.

Sometimes, the most difficult challenges are the ones that take place in the classroom. Children with AD/HD tend to struggle tremendously in the educational environment. Too often, school success becomes the cornerstone to the self-esteem of our children and how they are seen as individuals. As parents, it is our responsibility to prevent this perception. School performance is only one area of competence and should not be viewed as the most important indicator of an individual's success or potential. A lack of school success today is not an accurate predictor of the successes of tomorrow. Each child has an area of competence from which we can help them build strength and motivation.

AD/HD is a disability which often entitles our children to accommodations and services within the educational environment. As we learn appropriate tools and strategies, it is important that we share the information with teachers and administrators. We can support our children's educational growth through communication, participation and encouragement. Furthermore, we must be willing to monitor their progress and advocate for them along the way.

Attention-Deficit/Hyperactivity Disorder will continue to be a focal point in our lives and there is no escaping its impact on our families.

You and your child are on a beautiful journey together, and while it may have times of pain and crisis, it will also be full of love and enlightenment.

Tammy Young is an educator and the parent of two children with AD/HD. Ms. Young shares her personal journey in, "Slow Down So I Can Tell You I Love You: A Handbook for Parents of Children with AD/HD." She offers practical solutions to the issues inherent to AD/HD, including diagnosis, treatment, behavior management, educational interventions and legal rights. For more information, visit her website: www. livingwithadhd.com.

This article first appeared in Attention!® magazine, June 2002.

Starting School Off Right

By Anne Addison, M.B.A., N.H.A.

When I was a kid, I remember my big worries about the first day of school. At the top of the list was my fear of the bouncing hot dogs that were served every Thursday in the cafeteria. They were clearly not edible, which meant a long afternoon with a grumbling stomach. Hot dog worrying was followed by rubber shoe worrying—big, thick, black, not cool rubber shoes. They were thrust into my hands any day my mother saw even just one cloud in the sky.

There wasn't much I could do about the hot dogs except cross my fingers and hope that they weren't there. But the rubber shoes—now that was a different story. Before each school year began, I carefully scoped out the neighborhood to figure out which yard would serve as the ideal stash spot for my rubber shoes. I would always find a bush that saved me from boarding the bus with them on.

My rainy day shoe problem was solved with a little creativity, planning, preparation and a positive attitude. How I dealt with those rubber shoes turned out to be a really good life lesson. In fact, I still use it at the beginning of each school year. But now it's the beginning of school for my exceptional son.

For many of us with exceptional children, the first day of school presents all sorts of anxieties that make the rubber shoe dilemma look like, well, child's play. New teachers, a new education plan, new classmates, and maybe even a new school are a lot to take in for any child, and certainly for one who often finds new situations overwhelming.

Think about the beginning of school the way my mother approached rain. What was my mother really doing? She was teaching me how to think ahead and be prepared for the unexpected. Though the shoes were uncool, her heart was in the right place.

Beginning the school year on a positive note doesn't just happen. If you want your relationship with the teachers and those working with your child to be productive, you definitely need to get started off on the right foot. And the right foot is the one that steps forward with a positive heartset, proactive mindset and is committed to establishing good team habits right from the get go.

> What you see regarding your child at home, in the community and with outside therapists is invaluable information for the team.

Your child's success is highly dependent upon the effective functioning of the team that supports him. The team is not just his primary teacher, though you may see and communicate with him or her the most. The core team is made up of the people listed on your child's IEP and includes teachers, therapists and specialists. But it is also the lady behind the lunch counter who serves your child's lunch each day, the recess monitor and the office staff. All of these individuals can play an active role in supporting your child and working towards his goals. If you want the team—both the core team and the others involved with your child—to be successful, they can be. It may happen with or without you, but there is a far greater chance of success if you take an active, positive role in supporting the team. After all, you are a critical part of it.

You are an Integral Part of the Team

Most likely you and the school team already know this. But being integral is one thing, being integral and valuable is another. The level and manner of your involvement can significantly impact the team's attitude, interest and decision-making abilities throughout the year.

Sit back for a minute and think about the words you would like used to describe your contribution to the team at the end of the school year—supportive, participatory, open-minded and collaborative? If these are some of the words that came to mind, you are already in the mindset of an effective team player. You still have time to become a team player who can be a tremendous benefit to the team.

A parent who is seen as an asset to the school-based team often has these qualities:

♦ Believes she has responsibilities on the team and takes them seriously,
♦ Comes from a place of acceptance rather than of judgment,
♦ Is nurturing, supportive and genuinely interested in team members' concerns,
♦ Thinks win-win, even when there are points-of-view different from her own,
♦ Is open-minded, communicative and collaborative, and
♦ Has realistic expectations.

Take Your Job Seriously

Our son Jack has not had the smoothest of school experiences. It became clear very early on, that I would not be one of those mothers who walked her child to the bus stop, chatted nonchalantly with the other moms, and then waved good-bye to her child and looked forward to six hours of whatever work filled her day. My morning was more like this: drive Jack to school (he didn't want to take the special needs bus), walk him into school, get a small stomachache if and when he did something other than walk to the classroom and hang his coat on the peg. I spent the next five or so hours working in my consulting practice, but not just working. There was always a little pit in the bottom of my stomach, wondering and worrying if things were going okay at school or if I would be called to help handle an emergency. There were a couple of years where I spent more time at the school than I did at my desk.

Your involvement as the parent member of the team may change a bit each year, depending upon the type of year that your child is having. A tough year will call for more involvement; a good year will call for less.

Though you may have a sense of your level of involvement, your role and responsibility on the team may not be as clear to you. The teacher instructs, the therapist provides a specific service, the social worker works on social skills and perhaps serves as the day-to-day coordinator. If the team supporting your child this year is new to you or different from the one that developed the IEP, you might want to sit down with them, or a few key individuals from it, to clarify their expectations of your role and responsibilities.

Three Key Responsibilities of Parents

There are three key responsibilities that should be considered the minimum requirements for a parent's responsibilities on the team; however, there is no reason to think in terms of least responsibility. Though there is a school team leader, you too, can play a leading role. The more initiative you take, the greater your value to the team.

1. Being the Coordinator of Information

You have more information and more sources of important information about your child than anyone else. What you see regarding your child at home, in the community and with outside therapists is invaluable information for the team. You may discover strategies that are particularly effective, be the first one to spot an emerging issue, or have a better sense of some major behavior or social themes. You need to share this information with the school team in a clear, concise way. A short memo that consolidates your observations and those of others who are working with your child outside the school can be extremely useful.

Giving the school-based team a snapshot of your child's activities during the summer, highlighting the major issues and his or her achievements, and perhaps reviewing the IEP to see if any issues need to be immediately addressed, can save them time and guesswork in the first few weeks. This will be a busy time while they are getting to know your child along with 18 or so other students. You are a fountain of important information that can move the "getting to know you" process smoothly along.

I like to prepare quarterly memos for the school-based and outside teams that give them an overview of my child's progress. Asking team members to briefly write down or tell me the key goals that they are working on, gains that have been made, issues that have cropped up, and any concerns they have, allows me to coordinate the information for the team to see. You may want to provide phone numbers or e-mail addresses in the memo so that team members can contact each other. If you do not have the skills needed for this kind of communication, suggest the idea to the team and work with them to identify the best person for this job.

2. Establishing the Communication Link

Your amount of communication with the teacher depends upon your child's functioning level. Even a child with mild AD/HD will run into some kind of glitch from time to time. Don't wait for the issue to find its way to you.

> When the same thing is being done at home and at school, the messages are reinforced and your child can hear them more strongly.

Ask your child's teacher her preferred mode of communication and then use it prudently. I have been able to head off bad ideas and homework headaches by e-mailing Jack's teacher early in the morning. She checks her messages before the day begins and we are in sync before Jack's head pops through her classroom door.

3. Getting Your Child Ready to Learn

Have you ever thought about what shape your child goes to school in? Is he tired or well rested, is he anxious and worried because of what is going on at home, or is he relaxed and refreshed? Our job as parents is to teach our children good life habits. Letting your child eat what he wants, do his homework "whenever," go to bed when he feels like it and spend his free time however he pleases is not teaching or modeling anything. Training children with AD/HD who have a naturally harder time with the basic concepts of good habits—structure, time management and organization—is a necessity if you want them to be able to manage themselves later on in life.

If your child is working on specific behavior goals, they should be addressed at home and at school. Everyone needs to be on the same page, and doing this from day one makes sense. Sitting down with the teacher and any other key members of the school-based team early in the school year to review how the behavioral, emotional and social aspects of your child's plan will be handled gets all of you operating and responding in the same way. When the same thing is being done at home and at school, the messages are reinforced and your child can hear them more strongly.

Show the Team that You Care

Tangible ways of showing the school team that you appreciate their efforts can be easy and have huge benefits. They can be as simple as bringing muffins to a meeting, writing unexpected notes of thanks or just telling the teacher when you notice a gain.

There are other times when you may want to really recognize that they have done something particularly special. For example, there was the time that Jack lost the retainer he had only worn for two weeks when it was thrown out with his lunch in the school cafeteria. It was spaghetti and meatballs day—not a good day to lose a clear, red, four-inch appliance. The lunchroom monitor and one of Jack's teachers offered to join my son in the hunt for the retainer. The three of them donned plastic gloves, turned over the large grey bin, and began the search. The retainer was not found.

The next day I delivered gifts of bath salts to the two teachers with a note that said, "Thank you for going way above and beyond the call of duty."

Teachers go above and beyond the call many times that you do see, and many times that you don't. Be free with your praise, letting them know that you appreciate all they are doing on your child's behalf. A little note of thanks goes a long way.

Heartset

The heartset is the feeling that you have towards someone or something. If you begin the year off with an approach to the teacher that smacks of distrust and negativity, how do you think she will feel? It is true that respect is something that is typically earned over time. But if you take this approach with the school-based team, it may take you a good three or four months to get to this point. In the meantime, if you are questioning, second-guessing and sending other verbal and non-verbal messages that do not reflect trust or respect, you could actually sabotage the team.

This is one of those situations where you need to take a leap of faith and start off the relationship by giving respect freely. This does not mean that you should turn off your antennae and follow blindly. Be alert, be aware, but start off the year giving the team members the benefit of the doubt.

When my son was entering first grade, everyone was concerned about which teacher he would have. Jack had just completed a horrific year of kindergarten with an experimental combining of two special needs classes that were team-taught. One teacher took a leave of absence in the middle of the year and the other had an extended illness. The class was out of control and so was Jack. The school team knew we expected the most stellar of teachers for Jack's first grade experience. What we got was Mrs. Gresia, fresh out of college.

The first week, she sent home the communication journal filled with complaints. I began to get nervous. Negative feelings started creeping up and I began to not like her. I called my liaison at the board of education and explained my concern. She said she understood my nervousness, given the previous year's experience, but how about sitting back and giving her a chance. In the meantime, my liaison went in to give a little guidance to Jack's teacher. Mrs. Gresia ended up being one of the most remarkable teachers Jack has ever had. But had I become negative rather than putting a little trust in her before I truly felt it, I could have ruined the whole year for Jack.

Mindset

Your mindset is the compilation of your perceptions and attitudes towards something. For example, Johnnie walks into the first day of fourth grade and his teacher groans. She has heard about Johnnie from his previous teachers. The news has not been good. Before Johnnie does a single thing, his new teacher has already formed an impression, which has become an attitude, and a negative one at that.

Like heartset, it is important that your mindset be in the right place from the first day of school. You come to school each year with the baggage of the previous years' experiences. You can't help it. It is just part of the deal. What you can help is what you do with it. Being led by attitudes created in a different time and place is not fair to this year's team. Most likely you are used to being in a "fighting" mode, fighting for solutions and perhaps services with the school, fighting for cooperation and self-responsibility with your child, and maybe even fighting over it all with your spouse. Lots of negative attitudes can easily develop without your knowledge.

Heartset and mindset are closely connected. How you feel about individuals affects your attitude towards them, and your attitude affects your feelings about them. It doesn't matter which comes first, heartset or mindset, but it is important to realize that each influences the other.

The beginning of the school year is a good time for a little introspection. Look at how you think and feel about the school, the teachers and the team supporting your child, and clean up any bad attitudes. Maybe you believe that you have good reasons for thinking about them the way you do. It doesn't matter. A good relationship is the backbone of a good team. If you want to have a good relationship with the team, you need to change the way that you think about them.

Getting Off on the Right Foot Makes the Journey Easier

I never did get used to the hot dogs and you probably won't ever get used to the surprises and struggles that the beginning of school can present for your exceptional child. The better you work with the school team, the more support you will feel and the more coordinated the effort for your child will be. What better time to start the collaboration than the first day of school?

Anne Addison, M.B.A., N.H.A., is the author of "One Small Starfish: A Mother's Everyday Advice, Survival Tactics & Wisdom for Raising a Special Needs Child." She serves on the Board of Visitors of Georgetown University's School of Nursing and Health Studies and is a board member of Connecticut Autism Spectrum Resource Center. Her website is www.anneaddison.com.

This article first appeared in *Attention!*® magazine, August 2003.

Why Teachers Resist—Understanding Teacher Attitudes about AD/HD

By Terry Illes, Ph.D.

As a school psychologist for more than 20 years, I have specialized in the assessment and treatment of children with AD/HD. As part of my professional responsibilities, I teach a class on the school management of AD/HD attended primarily by parents. We spend much of our class time discussing effective classroom accommodations (e.g., curriculum, instructional and behavioral interventions) for children with AD/HD. After teaching this class for a few years, I realized that knowledge did not always translate into practice. Indeed, parents often became discouraged as they encountered teacher resistance to implementing the classroom interventions they had learned in class. This is particularly frustrating because researchers have learned much during the last decade about the types of interventions that are effective in the management of AD/HD symptoms and most are readily available to teachers.

In this article, I will examine an underlying and subtle basis for such teacher resistance. I must emphasize that resistance to implementing proven interventions for children with AD/HD is not unique to teachers.

In fact, I experience a similar resistance from parents during a class that I also teach on home management of AD/HD. However, because my professional experience is primarily within the school setting, in this article I will focus on teacher resistance. I also believe that the basis for parent and teacher resistance is similar and that parents will discover much about their own parenting behavior as they read this article.

A Fundamental Bias: If It's Behavior, It's a Matter of Choice

I believe that teacher resistance is due to a fundamental bias in the way teachers view children with behavioral disabilities. This view is embedded in what psychologists call "a theory of mind." A theory of mind describes the set of assumptions or inferences that people use to make sense of someone else's behavior. For example, if you observe a young child throwing a tantrum in a store as a chagrined adult angrily looks on, you may infer that the child is upset because his/her parent has denied something of value (e.g., candy or a toy) to the child. This is an attempt to make sense of our social world.

We rely on the fundamental assumption that an individual's overt behavior is motivated and under the control of the person performing the behavior. Indeed, it is this assumption that allows society to hold individuals accountable

> When teachers fall into the trap of the Behavioral Model of Disability, it is not out of indifference or hostility. Rather, it is a mindset that seems to come to us naturally as we attempt to interpret human behavior.

for their actions. By contrast, it is also obvious that some behaviors occur unintentionally, and the assumption of control is readily suspended. For example, if you observe a young child shaking spasmodically in a store with a scared adult helplessly looking on, you probably will infer that the child has some type of disorder that is causing an involuntary motor response.

In other cases, the connection between behavior and intent is unclear, and the observer must make an informed guess as to the role of intention. School-related problems, whether academic or behavioral, often fit into this category, and I believe that teachers apply different "theories of mind" when attempting to understand the basis for academic and behavioral problems. In fact, these differing mindsets often determine a teacher's willingness or disposition to make classroom accommodations for students with problems.

The Behavioral vs. the Academic Models of Disability

I developed the Behavioral and Academic Models of Disability (Illes, 2001) to draw attention to the different sets of assumptions that teachers (or parents) use to understand children with academic or behavioral problems. The Behavioral Model summarizes the characteristic manner in which teachers respond to students with learning difficulties:

In the Behavioral Model, a teacher observes a student to have a behavior problem; then the teacher assumes that the behavior is linked to the student's motivation (such as the need for negative attention).

If the behavior can be attributed to motivation, then it must be voluntary

and premeditated and, thus, the teacher reacts with anger because the student intended to misbehave.

The belief that the "bad" behavior was deliberate further leads the teacher to attempt to "stamp out" or eliminate the problem behavior. The process of elimination suggests that it is the student who must do the changing. The focus will be on stopping a behavior rather than on teaching new skills, the change will be rapid and negative consequences— or punishment—will be used to encourage this change. Thus, there is no need to make special accommodations for the child with AD/HD.

The assumptions made by teachers regarding students with behavioral disabilities stand in stark contrast to the Academic Model.

In the Academic Model, a student is observed to have a learning problem; then the teacher assumes that the learning deficit has an underlying neurological basis. If the deficit is neurological, then the problem must be involuntary. Thus, the teacher believes that the student would perform better if possible, and because the student is perceived to be a victim of neurological circumstances beyond his/her

> Teachers apply the Behavioral and Academic Models indiscriminately and without giving the matter much consideration. When challenged about the justification for doing so, most teachers react with surprise.

control, the teacher reacts with empathy.

The teacher intuitively understands that the student would prefer to be as academically successful as other students. And, finally, this insight directs the teacher to remediate or fix the student's learning problem. The process of remediation suggests that the educational system will accept responsibility for the student's change, the focus of change will be on skill building, the change will be gradual and that positive consequences will be used to reinforce this progress.

Teachers apply the Behavioral and Academic Models indiscriminately and without giving the matter much consideration. When challenged about the justification for doing so, most teachers react with surprise. Indeed, they usually feel that the reason is obvious (although vague) and is supported by supposed research that indicates that learning problems are caused by an organic problem in the brain but that behavior problems are not. Ironically, there may be as much research to support the neurological basis of AD/HD as there is to support the neurological basis of a specific learning disability such as a reading disorder.

What You Can Do as a Parent

It is my overwhelming experience that teachers share with parents a genuine concern for children with AD/HD. When teachers fall into the trap of the Behavioral Model, it is not out of indifference or hostility. Rather, it is a

mindset that seems to come to us naturally as we attempt to interpret human behavior. Parents who honestly examine their own behavior may discover that they often commit the same mistake in judgment when dealing with their child with AD/HD. Consequently, parents may first need to elevate a teacher's awareness of his or her underlying attitudes about students with AD/HD before they can expect teachers to implement specialized classroom accommodations.

As part of this effort, parents must be prepared to use strategies to help teachers understand the different sets of assumptions that are falsely applied to students with learning and behavioral problems. Parents who approach teacher resistance out of an alliance with teachers will be much more successful than parents who approach the problem from an adversarial position. Some strategies to help accomplish this include:

1. **Know yourself.** As parents, there are probably times when you are falling into the trap of viewing your child's behavior from the perspective of the Behavioral Model. Do you get angry with your child for running up and down the stairs instead of walking? Do you find yourself losing patience when your child interrupts you or seems to talk incessantly? Do you tell yourself that it was okay to be upset with your child because you know that he/she could have chosen to behave differently? Parents who are aware of their own biases will be more likely to discern this behavior in teachers.

2. **Be a resource.** By providing teachers with evidence about the medical basis of AD/HD, you may help them to understand the fallacies reflected in the Behavioral Model.

3. **Provide a visual cue.** A metaphor can serve as a great tool to trigger understanding and acceptance of an elusive concept. I have used "behavioral seizures"

as a metaphor to encourage teachers to apply the Academic Model to children with AD/HD. I ask them to imagine a student with a seizure disorder. If the student did not have a seizure on Monday or Tuesday, but did on Wednesday, would the teacher or parent punish the child for the seizure activity on Wednesday? Of course, they respond that it would be ridiculous and unfair to do so because the child has no control over his or her seizure activity. At this time, I review the evidence on the medical origins of AD/HD. I then ask the teacher to visualize that the student is experiencing a "behavioral seizure" whenever the student is acting inappropriately. I have had many teachers tell me that this visual strategy has helped them to be more sympathetic and understanding when the child with AD/HD is experiencing problems with self-control.

4. **Use AD/HD as an explanation, not a justification.** Sometimes parents respond to the problems of their children in such a way that they encourage teachers to rely on the Behavioral Model. One mistake that almost certainly triggers this reaction is when parents appear to use AD/HD as a reason to excuse their child's inappropriate behavior rather than as a basis for understanding it. Teachers who believe that AD/HD is falsely being used to excuse a child from responsibility will be more likely to insist on applying the Behavioral Model to restore the child's accountability. Therefore, I encourage parents to openly discuss this issue with teachers and to reassure teachers that they accept and support the need to hold their child accountable for inappropriate behavior. Once teachers are confident of this support, I find that they are much more receptive to later discussions about the most effective and fair ways to teach this skill.

5. **Make the teacher a partner.** Teachers who have accurate information about a student will be more likely to treat that child fairly. Offer the teacher information about AD/HD and your child's past difficulties. Make sure to include the teacher as a collaborative member of the treatment team. Demonstrate to the teacher that you value his or her opinion and input when making treatment decisions about your child. You will find that teachers who feel part of the decision-making process will be more understanding and willing to accept the Academic Model as a guide to helping your child.

> I ask the teacher to visualize that the student is experiencing a "behavioral seizure" whenever the student is acting inappropriately. Many teachers tell me that this visual strategy has helped them to be more sympathetic and understanding.

Terry Illes, Ph.D., has been employed as a school psychologist with the Jordan School District in the Salt Lake City area for over 20 years. Dr. Illes conducts numerous workshops and classes on AD/HD in the Salt Lake area and is currently working as part of a collaborative team on improving the quality of care for children with AD/HD within the community. Dr. Illes is on the CHADD Board of Directors, 2005–2008.

This article first appeared in *Attention!®* magazine, June 2004.

A 24-Month Follow-up to the NIMH MTA Study

By 13 Members of the MTA Steering Committee:

Peter S. Jensen, M.D.
Howard B. Abikoff, Ph.D.
L. Eugene Arnold, M.D.
Jeffrey Epstein, Ph.D.

Laurence L. Greenhill, M.D.
Lily Hechtman, M.D.
Stephen P. Hinshaw, Ph.D.
John S. March, M.D.
Jeffrey H. Newcorn, M.D.

James M. Swanson, Ph.D.
Benedetto Vitiello, M.D.
Karen Wells, Ph.D.
Timothy Wigal, Ph.D.

Over the last four years the National Institute of Mental Health (NIMH) Multimodal Treatment study of Children with AD/HD—or MTA for short—has received a great deal of attention in scientific literature and the mainstream press. One of the largest treatment studies ever funded by the NIMH for either children or adults, the MTA brought together nationally recognized authorities in AD/HD at six different universities and medical centers to evaluate the leading treatments for AD/HD, including behavior therapy and medication, over a longer time period than is usually studied. As members of the Steering Committee of the MTA for NIMH, we are pleased to provide an overview of the initial results, along with a preview of new findings observed at the 24-month follow up assessment.

Background

The MTA study included 579 elementary school children with AD/HD, ages seven to nine, randomly assigned to one of four treatment conditions implemented over a 14-month period:

- **medication alone** (medication was carefully adjusted for maximum benefit for each child, with monthly visits with the doctor to check on the child's progress);

- **psychosocial/behavioral treatment alone** (including an integrated program of specific intervention with the children and extensive training on this approach for parents and teachers);
- **a combination of both;** or
- **routine community care** (that is, whatever treatments were accessible to families in their community setting).

The study was designed to answer three critical questions:
1. What treatments work best while they are implemented?
2. Which treatments are best in the long term?
3. Are the intensive treatments offered in the MTA research protocol better than the treatment options accessible in the community (often limited by obstacles in the "real world" such as lack of insurance coverage)?

We assessed outcomes in several different domains: the symptoms of AD/HD, aggressive behaviors, anxious/depressed behaviors, parent-child relations, peer and social skills and academic achievement.

Review of Initial Findings (14 months)

At the end of 14 months, children in all treatment groups tended to improve (all were treated; there was no untreated control group). However, there were significant differences in outcome among the groups and treatment approaches. The initial results, published in December 1999, showed that long-term combination treatments as well as medication management alone were both significantly superior to intensive behavioral treatment alone and/or routine community treatments in reducing AD/HD symptoms. Most (two-thirds) of the group assigned to the community care group received the same type of medication (stimulants) prescribed by the MTA staff, but the way the medication was managed differed, with monthly office visits providing frequent contact between the MTA physicians and families and monthly telephone contact with teachers. The community treatment physician, by contrast, generally saw the child only one to two times per year, and for shorter periods of time each visit and usually did not have any direct interaction with the teachers. Perhaps the most significant difference was that the community physicians prescribed lower doses of medication.

Based on these findings, we concluded that for AD/HD symptoms, a closely monitored medication management approach of the MTA was superior to behavioral treatment alone and to routine community care that included medication. Combined treatment offered slightly greater benefits than medication management alone for AD/HD symptom reduction as well as for other domains, such as peer relations, parent-child relations and academic outcomes. The combination treatment was significantly better than medication alone for a global outcome measure that included all six outcome areas noted above, achieving this effect with 20% lower doses than that required for the medication-only group. For some children, particularly those who also had parent reported anxiety problems and additional behavior problems, the combined treatment worked relatively better than the medication or behavior therapy alone. It also aided the social skills of the most economically disadvantaged children in the study more than did the other treatments.

While findings at the 14-month stage were significant, several key questions remained with respect to the lasting benefits of the interventions after the MTA-delivered treatments had stopped, and all families were faced with the challenges and decisions of pursuing care as normally offered in the community.

> Combined treatment offered slightly greater benefits than medication management alone.

- Would the initial treatment effects found at 14 months continue, even after the intensive MTA-type treatments were stopped?
- Would the greater effectiveness of intensive medication treatment over behavior therapy continue, or would behavior therapy eventually "catch up?"
- Would the child's having received the earlier combination of medication and behavior therapy prove to be better than having received medication alone?

Ongoing Follow-up Findings

To address these questions, the MTA group continued to monitor—though not treat—all children and families who participated in the initial 14-month treatment phase. At 24 months, we evaluated the children's outcomes based on their initially assigned groups, generally finding that outcomes for the combined and medication management groups were superior to the behavior therapy and community-care groups. While the relative superiority was reduced by 50 percent, children who had received the MTA medication alone approach were still better off than children who received the intensive behavior therapy alone (at home and at school). This was particularly true for AD/HD symptoms and oppositional/aggressive symptoms based on ratings by teachers (who were not part of the initial treatment component of the study) as well as by parents. Based on this, we concluded that the benefits of intensive medication management for AD/HD extended 10 months beyond the intensive treatment phase, although the effects appeared to diminish over time.

We also conducted analyses of potential side effects, especially those related to height and weight, areas that have been a concern to parents for decades. Previous studies have suggested that such effects—that is, medication-related reductions in height and weight growth rates—are short-term, but disappear by the time the child has become an adult. We did find at both the 14- and 24-month assessment points that height and weight were affected. The following letter, sent this fall to all parents of children in the MTA study, addressed this issue upfront.

For many years, there have been concerns about the effects of stimulant medication on growth. Some initial studies suggested that growth was reduced by stimulant medication in the short-term, but not in the long-term. To measure these effects in the MTA follow-up, at each assessment we have measured the children's heights and weights to look for any growth suppression in the short run (first year), the "middle run" (second year), and the long run (third year and beyond).

One way that we did this was to compare a group of the children in the MTA who used medication consistently over the two years (the continuously medicated group) to a group of the children who never used medication (the never medicated group). We found that the continuously medicated group grew more slowly than the never medicated group—about 0.75 inch (¾ of an inch) less in

height (an increase of 4.10 inches vs. 4.85 inches) and 8.5 pounds less in weight (an increase of 13.5 lbs. versus 22.0 lbs. in weight) over those two years.

We also compared the growth rates of children in the study to national norms. The never medicated group grew faster than the national average (about ½ inch more than expected), whereas the continuously medicated group grew slightly slower than the national average (about ¼ inch less than expected) over the two-year period.

We are now working to find out whether the growth patterns we have shown for the "middle run" (two years) will continue over a longer time period (three years or more). We do not have such information ready right now, but we will let you know when we have some definite findings to report about this important question.

If your adolescent is taking stimulant medication, we suggest that you share this letter with the physician prescribing the medication and ask him or her to read the articles in the April 2004 issue of *Pediatrics*. Along with a regular tracking of height and weight, this may help in the regular evaluation of what is the best treatment plan for your adolescent.

The use of medication is an individual decision best made by each family in consultation with the child's doctor. Even though medication appears to incur some risks in terms of slowing growth in height and weight, available evidence indicates that the symptoms of untreated AD/HD also pose other risks that have been documented in follow-up studies of AD/HD, including increased chance of school failure, poor peer interactions, problems with substance abuse, juvenile delinquency, car accidents, etc.

Parents and caregivers have to consider the tradeoffs in the face of uncertainties—the uncertainty of not knowing "for sure" whether there are (or the magnitude of) long-term effects on height and weight and the uncertainty of whether stopping an effective medication treatment will result in the return of or increase in a child's difficulties.

Although the children who received medication demonstrated reduced symptoms of AD/HD, they also experienced some effects on weight and height (with height effects ranging from ¼ to ¾ inch at the 24-month assessment, depending upon the comparison group used to estimate this effect). Of note, some AD/HD investigators have suggested that such growth suppression effects are seen mainly only after a child first starts medication, after which more normal growth rates resume, but the MTA study showed that these effects are manifested at least into the second year of treatment. We cannot yet predict with certainty whether such effects will persist past that point, but because we are following these children into adolescence and young adulthood, our future reports should provide more definitive information on the issue of whether there are persisting effects on long-term growth outcomes.

Disclaimer: The opinions contained in this article are the private views of the authors and are not to be construed as official or as reflecting the views of the National Institute of Mental Health, the National Institutes of Health, or the Department of Health and Human Services.

Disclosure: Although the MTA Study was supported entirely by federal funds, most of the MTA investigators receive research support or consulting/speaking fees from pharmaceutical companies distributing medications for AD/HD.

> The use of medication is an individual decision best made by each family in consultation with the child's doctor.

This article first appeared in *Attention!*® magazine, December 2003.

Start a CHADD Support Group in Your Community

Managing AD/HD every day is a challenge for any family or adult with AD/HD. Coming together with others who are facing the same challenges can be an enormous benefit for all who participate. If you are interested in starting a parent or adult support group in your community, contact the Chapter Services Department at CHADD at (301) 306-7070 ext 121 or go online to www.chadd.org\supportgroups. We will send you a Support Group Toolkit with everything you need to get started.

Stimulant Medication: Side Effects on Children

by Glen R. Elliot, Ph.D., M.D.

Stimulants are a class of medication widely used to treat attention-deficit/hyperactivity disorder (AD/HD). There also is a non-stimulant alternative medication for the treatment of AD/HD; however, this article focuses specifically on stimulant medications. Dozens of studies over the years have documented that stimulants promptly enhance focus, improve impulse control and decrease excessive physical activity in 65 to 85 percent of children with AD/HD.[1,2] Stimulants have been shown to counteract the common consequences of AD/HD. For example, school performance has generally improved for children taking medication.

The two major classes of stimulants available in the United States are methylphenidate (Concerta, Focalin, Metadate, Methylin, Ritalin, Ritalin LA) and amphetamine (Dexedrine, Dextrostat, Adderall, Adderall XR). Methylphenidate and amphetamine have similar effects, including benefits and side effects. Used in various forms since the early 1960s, the most dramatic changes in use have occurred in the past decade as effective long-acting forms have become available.

Stimulants have been popular not only because they work well but also because they have several attractive features, including rapid onset of action and well-documented safety. Still, they are not always free of side effects. This article reviews some of the common side effects associated with stimulants and explores ways to avoid or minimize them.

The observations about side effects are drawn largely from an ongoing research project through the National Institute of Mental Health (NIMH) called the Multimodal Treatment Study of Children with AD/HD (MTA), which is now reporting on experiences with a group of children with the disorder who have been followed for six years.[3] Consistent with findings from similar research, the MTA is one of the longest and largest studies available for AD/HD.

Appetite and Weight

Appetite suppression and resulting weight loss are common side effects. The effect is dose dependent, with over a third of patients complaining of decreased appetite at doses of 50 mg a day or higher. Typically, the effect is immediate, subsiding as the level of medication in the body decreases throughout the day. Many individuals find that this side effect is temporary and diminishes over time, even when the dosage level is maintained. Appetite loss is not universal, but few if any patients seem to experience an appetite increase.

Decreased food consumption results in weight loss or at least failure to gain weight at expected rates. This effect clearly can continue for months to years, but data from the MTA

> The most common approach to addressing appetite loss, and therefore weight, is to teach children to eat when they are hungry.

suggests that the effect is greatest after patients had taken the medication for 1½ years. At 14 and 24 months, the difference in weight was approximately 10–12 pounds between those on the highest amount of medication compared to those on the lowest. After six years on the medication, the difference was less than four pounds.

The most common approach to addressing appetite loss, and therefore weight, is to teach children to eat when they are hungry. Thus, a good breakfast, eaten before the medication takes effect, is key. Appetite usually returns by dinner time; if it does not, a healthy before-bedtime snack is useful. Medication-free holidays on weekends and school vacations and during the summer also can assist in maintaining weight, assuming the child's behavior makes that feasible.

Height

The impact of sustained stimulant use on height has been and remains controversial. Over the past two decades, scientific evidence seems to have pointed variously to significant effects, no effects and reversible effects. The MTA and several other studies now seem to suggest that, on average, children taking stimulants gain height more slowly than those not taking stimulants. In the MTA, a comparison of growth after two years in the study showed that children with AD/HD who never received medications actually were growing faster than children in the control group (who were matched by age, gender and school), while those who took a stimulant throughout the two years gained height at a slower rate. The result was a 1-inch difference in height at two years

between the unmedicated and medicated groups; however, after six years, there was no marked difference in height between the two groups.[4] Parents may want to monitor their child's growth, and pediatricians have growth charts to make that easier.

Insomnia

Insomnia is a common side effect of stimulants, although 15 percent of individuals, with or without AD/HD, actually seem to sleep better with stimulants. Severity of the insomnia is dose related and typically diminishes over time. Still, the MTA showed that, on average, use of stimulants led to a 30-minute delay of sleep onset among some during the first weeks.

Reasonable strategies for dealing with insomnia, if it is a problem, include trying a lower dose, a shorter-acting version of the same stimulant or a different stimulant. Also important are matters of "sleep hygiene," that is, making sure the child is in an environment conducive to sleep and has nighttime habits that encourage sleep. Long-term use of a second medication strictly to aid sleep is not uncommon, but no good research exists about either the safety of this practice or the quality of the medication-induced sleep.

Rebound

As the medication wears off, the child's behaviors not only return to off-drug levels but actually grow worse for a time that may last up to several hours. This is known as rebound and its effect is poorly understood in some children. Rebound is most often described with children taking short-acting forms of the stimulants. The effect is not clearly dose-related, nor is it clear that rebound diminishes with time.

Long-acting formulations seem to help diminish rebound, as may a smaller dose of an immediate-acting form 30 to 60 minutes before rebound occurs. Trying a different stimulant also may work.

Tics

Many boys, whether they are on stimulant medication or not, develop tics. A simple motor tic might be an involuntary eye blink or facial grimace. Complex motor tics are not as common and might be something like a hair-smoothing gesture or shoulder shrug. Vocal tics are involuntary sounds that range from clucking to actual bursts of phrases. In addition, Tourette Syndrome, a neurological disorder with a specific form of tics, often presents with signs and symptoms of AD/HD before the tics emerge. Further, it is clear that, at least acutely, stimulants are apt to worsen the severity of tics when present and to "uncover" tics in people at risk for having them. Less clear are the long-term effects of stimulants on tics. Best available evidence now suggests that acute worsening of tics does not lead to long-term bad outcomes; in fact, some research suggests that stimulants actually may decrease tic severity over the long term.[5] Still, parents and physicians understandably are reluctant to prescribe medication that may make tics more severe.

Depending on the child's need and the severity of the tics, parents may want to consider switching to a different stimulant, trying a nonstimulant medication for treating the AD/HD or continuing to use a stimulant for the condition while adding another medication to suppress the tics. Each approach has its proponents and potential uses.

Cognitive Blunting

In the MTA, 25 percent of children starting on stimulants experienced cognitive blunting, which refers to a change in mental functioning characterized by an apparent slowing of thinking and distant subdued responses to events going on around them. The effect was dose-dependent but could occur even at the lowest dose. It sometimes seemed to lessen with time, but not always.

Approaches to cognitive blunting include decreasing the dose, provided it still can provide adequate behavioral benefit. Sometimes, after several weeks or months, an increased dose will not result in a return of this side effect. Switching to a different stimulant also can work. Otherwise, a nonstimulant medication for AD/HD may be the best approach.

Irritability

Parents often describe children on stimulants as being more irritable and edgy. Although this certainly can be true, the MTA titration trial showed that the highest reports of irritability were for placebo, where no medication was actually administered, with decreasing ratings as stimulant dose increased. Therefore, parents should look for timing effects to determine if irritability appears as the stimulant is building up or wearing off or is really at its worst when the stimulant is in full effect.

Again, irritability often seems to lessen with time. If it does not, trying a different type of stimulant or even a different preparation of the same stimulant may be worthwhile.

Summary

Stimulant medications can be highly beneficial for people with AD/HD but are not without potential adverse effects. Parents must be able to speak freely with the prescribing physician about such side effects and should be able to work with the physician both to monitor for such effects and to intervene promptly if they occur.

Notes

[1]Jensen, P.S. (2001). Findings from the NIMH Multimodal Treatment Study of AD/HD (MTA): Implications and applications for primary care providers. *Journal of Developmental and Behavioral Pediatrics, 22:*60–73.

[2]Swanson, J.M., et al. (2001). Clinical relevance of the primary findings of the MTA: Success rates based on severity of AD/HD and ODD symptoms at the end of treatment. *Journal of the American Academy of Child and Adolescent Psychiatry, 40:*168–179.

[3]MTA Cooperative Group. (2004). National Institute of Mental Health Multimodal Treatment Study of AD/HD follow-up: 24-month outcomes of treatment strategies for attention-deficit/hyperactivity disorder. *Pediatrics, 113:*754–761.

[4]MTA Cooperative Group (2004). National Institute of Mental Health Multimodal Treatment Study of AD/HD follow-up: Changes in effectiveness and growth after the end of treatment. *Pediatrics, 113:*762–769.

[5]Treatment of AD/HD in children with tics: a randomized controlled trial. (2002). *Neurology, 58:*527–536.3-10

Glen R. Elliott, Ph.D., M.D., is a child and adolescent psychiatrist and has been director of the Children's Center at Langley Porter at the University of California, San Francisco, since 1989. He also is one of the principal investigators in the NIMH-sponsored study, Multimodal Treatment of AD/HD.

This article first appeared in *Attention!*® magazine, April 2005.

Your Vehicle Donation Will Lower Your Taxes and Benefit CHADD

There is an easy and convenient way to donate your used car, truck, RV, SUV, motorcycle or boat to CHADD and get a tax deduction. Through the CHADD National Car Donation Program, all of the work is done for you at no charge: quick towing service, title processing, appraisal (if required), sale at auction or dismantler, accounting and a receipt for tax purposes.

You can make your vehicle donation to CHADD through our partnership with the nonprofit organization Volunteers of America. Visit www.carshelpingpeople.org/chadd for more details and an online application or call toll free at 1-800-948-1414. When making an online donation, please be sure to include the "/chadd" at the end of the Web site address. If phoning in your donation, you must indicate that CHADD is your designated charity for CHADD to benefit.

CHADD chapters are eligible to receive 25 percent of the net proceeds of vehicles donated by members to CHADD National. Any non-member donor is welcome to contact the Development Department at CHADD to designate a chapter to get 25 percent of the net proceeds.

Your vehicle donation will be greatly appreciated and will support the CHADD mission to improve the lives of people affected by Attention-Deficit/Hyperactivity Disorder.

CHADD®
CHILDREN AND ADULTS WITH
ATTENTION-DEFICIT/
HYPERACTIVITY DISORDER

Chapter 4
AD/HD in Adolescents

The Transition to Middle School

by Steven W. Evans, Ph.D., Zewelanji Serpell, Ph.D., and Casey White

The transition to middle school brings exciting but challenging experiences for both parents and children, particularly those children with attention-deficit/hyperactivity disorder (AD/HD). Parents often approach this shift with great trepidation as they watch and foster their child's growing independence, while simultaneously wondering whether there is such a thing as "normal" development during the middle school years. In fact, the term "maturation" may seem counterintuitive given the nature of the many changes children experience at this age.

> Children with AD/HD are vulnerable to obstacles associated with the social and academic demands of middle school.

Middle school affords new opportunities for choice, ranging from selecting elective classes to making decisions about how to behave in unsupervised situations such as hallways and bathrooms, and in situations involving opportunities for experimenting with drugs and alcohol or engaging in sexual behavior and delinquent activities. However, along with these choices, come higher expectations to demonstrate independence, exercise self-control and make wise decisions. Many students are unprepared to cope with the responsibilities of independence as they struggle with the emotional and physical changes associated with puberty that already make this developmental stage difficult.

The amount of adult monitoring dramatically decreases in middle school, and the change in the student/teacher relationship is one of the most significant factors affecting children's transition. Middle school teachers are expected to know over 100 students whom they see for short intervals of time resulting in limited knowledge about each student. In addition, teachers do not consistently observe students during transitions between classes, trips to the restroom and at recess.

Furthermore, while elementary school teachers are told about problems in settings in which they do not accompany the child—such as the bus or cafeteria—most middle schools do not have a designated individual who serves as the repository of such information. Therefore, no one person in middle school monitors progress and problems closely, adjusts expectations in response to stressful situations or addresses situations in a big picture context. These and other student supports associated with the role elementary school teachers play are what keep many children with AD/HD afloat during their early years of schooling. The removal of this valuable safety net can have a detrimental effect on success, and children with AD/HD are left especially vulnerable to obstacles associated with the social and academic demands of middle school.

Academic Challenges

The academic expectations for independence, organization and task completion without the support of the caring elementary school teacher can make the transition to middle school academically challenging. One of the most obvious areas affected by the increased expectation is the management of assignments and preparation for tests and quizzes. Organizational challenges are further complicated by the varying behavioral and academic expectations from teacher to teacher and class to class. Students are frequently given assignment notebooks along with prompts and reminders, but the organizational demands on middle school students with AD/HD may lead to frustration and failure. Parents often become frustrated at not knowing what is due and when tests will occur and therefore feel unable to help their child. Many students complicate things further by presenting their parents with excuses about why they do not have to complete the work in their notebook or why the note from the teacher about missing assignments is not a true problem.

Many students also experience difficulties with studying and comprehension. Passive and inefficient study habits are common among youth with AD/HD. As a result, even when they remember a test and bring home the materials to study, their preparation time can yield disappointing results. Middle school students are also typically required to do more independent writing than is required in elementary school. Sometimes this takes the form of short answer or essay questions on tests and assignments; at other times it involves writing reports or stories. These can be challenging tasks because written language requires the organization of thoughts into phrases, sentences and paragraphs and *attention to the details* of grammar, spelling and punctuation. These tend to be weak areas for middle school students with AD/HD, and their written products are frequently deficient.

Social Challenges

While the academic challenges may be more obvious, the social demands upon adolescents are no less daunting. The middle school years are socially challenging for even the most socially skilled students. Loyalty between friends is frequently compromised by the opportunity to gain social acceptance from others by revealing a secret or blemish about a friend. Behavior exhibited by one child may gain quick acceptance as humorous by peers while the same behavior exhibited by a less accepted student may be ridiculed and lead to the ostracizing of the unskilled student. Conformity with style, knowledge about the latest music and sports trivia and recognition of the ever-changing social status of peers are keys to a child's social acceptance among peers. Social success in early adolescence requires mastery of an incredibly complex set of skills and knowledge.

Children with AD/HD often experience problems with peer interactions because they lack understanding of these complexities, including reading the social behaviors of peers and recognizing the cause and effect relationships between their behavior and the behavior of others. Students with AD/HD-predominantly combined-type are especially at risk for social rejection, as they may come across as intrusive, disruptive and aggressive. For example, in conversations they may annoy their peers by interrupting, talking excessively or forgetting what others have said. As a result of such behaviors, many students with AD/HD experience active peer rejection in the form of teasing and bullying or are simply ignored. Similar problems often occur with teacher-student relationships, and these may be further compromised by problems these students have with authority.

Social deficits vary greatly among children with AD/HD, but those with obvious social problems are particularly at risk for making poor decisions regarding smoking and other

> The middle school years are socially challenging for even the most socially skilled students.

substance use. In middle school many children have their first exposure to alcohol, tobacco and other substances, and they frequently receive a lot of peer pressure to experiment. Youth with AD/HD tend to have unrealistic impressions of their peers' attitudes and may experiment because they think everyone is doing it. Middle school youth also have a limited understanding of how the choices they make regarding peers influence their behaviors. As a consequence, many engage in sexual behaviors, delinquent acts and substance use as a means of being accepted into social groups they perceive as popular or "cool."

Preparing for the Transition

Despite the challenges associated with the middle school years, many students with AD/HD surmount the difficulties and demonstrate success. Parents play an important role in preparing their child for, and guiding them through, the middle school transition. Relatively simple steps such as establishing a homework management plan, monitoring friendship patterns and facilitating positive social interactions can make a big difference in the developmental process. It is important for parents of youth with AD/HD to recognize that this is a difficult developmental stage for the vast majority of children (and their parents). Some of the most helpful things parents can do to prepare for this transition include knowing what to expect, advocating for their child, managing their own stress and mental health, and finding ways to accept their child and show that they love him or her

despite the problems. A couple of helpful resources for parents and children are listed at the end of this article.

Resources

Robin, A.L. (1998). *AD/HD in Adolescents.* New York: The Guilford Press.

Zeigler-Dendy, C.A. & Zeigler, A. (2003). *A Bird's-Eye View of Life with ADD and AD/HD: Advice from Young Survivors.* Cedar Bluff, Alabama: Cherish the Children.

Steven W. Evans, Ph.D., is an associate professor of psychology at the Alvin V. Baird Attention & Learning Disabilities Center at James Madison University. He conducts treatment outcome research for adolescents with AD/HD. Dr. Evans is a member of the CHADD Professional Advisory Board, 2004–2007.

Zewelanji Serpell, Ph.D., is a developmental psychologist and associate director of research for the Challenging Horizons Program, a school-based treatment program for adolescents with AD/HD, housed in the Alvin V. Baird Attention & Learning Disabilities Center at James Madison University.

Casey White is a graduate student in the Psychological Sciences Program at James Madison University. She supervises an afterschool treatment program for adolescents with AD/HD and assists with the coordination of research projects.

This article first appeared in *Attention!®* magazine, June 2005.

Surviving the Ride—Parenting Teenagers with AD/HD (Part 1 of 2)

By Chris A. Zeigler Dendy, M.S.

Parenting a teenager with AD/HD may be compared to riding a roller coaster: there are many ups and downs, laughs and tears, and breathtaking and terrifying experiences. Although parents crave calm, uneventful weeks, the norm with these teens is more likely unsettling highs and lows. Without a doubt, raising sons with AD/HD has been the most humbling and challenging experience of my life. Even with my background as a veteran teacher, school psychologist, mental health counselor and administrator with over 30 years experience, I often felt inadequate and doubted my parenting decisions.

Parenting these children is not easy for anyone! A wise child psychiatrist once observed, "I'm so glad I had the opportunity to raise 'an easy child' in addition to my child with AD/HD. Otherwise, I would have always doubted my parenting skills." Obviously, there are no simple parenting or counseling answers. We all—the child, parents and professionals—struggle with the best way to treat this condition.

During adolescence, the "job descriptions" for parents and teens are often in conflict. The parents' primary job is to gradually *decrease* their control, "letting go" of their teenager with grace and skill. In contrast, the teenager's main job is to begin the process of separating from his parents and become an independent, responsible adult. For better or worse, part of the teen's job is to experiment with making his own decisions, testing limits and exercising his judgment. When the teen starts this process, parents may feel they are "losing control." Ironically, the natural tendency is to exert *even more* control. After all, giving freedom and responsibility to teenagers with AD/HD is enough to unnerve even the most stouthearted parent.

Unfortunately for teens with AD/HD, several factors complicate the process of growing up. First and foremost, the **two to four year developmental delay** exhibited by most teens with an attention deficit often causes problems. A 15-year-old may act as though he were 11, but thinks he should have the privileges of a 21-year-old. They are more impulsive than their classmates and seldom think of consequences before they act. Chronologically (by virtue of age), teenagers with AD/HD are ready to assume their independence; developmentally (by virtue of maturity) they are not.

Secondly, they are more **difficult to discipline** than their peers; they do not learn from rewards and punishment as easily as other teens. Early on, parents learn that punishment alone is ineffective. Furthermore, use of physical punishment is no longer a viable parenting strategy. Behavioral interventions effective in childhood such as, "time out" or "stars and charts," lose much of their effectiveness during the teen years. Unfortunately, their emotionality, low frustration tolerance and tendency to "blow up" make it difficult to resolve problems calmly.

Third, **coexisting problems** such as learning disabilities, sleep disturbances, depression or executive function deficits are extremely common and make it more difficult to develop an effective treatment plan.

With all these challenges, we parents worry greatly about our children. What does the future hold? Will our teenager ever graduate from high school, much less go to college? Will he or she be able to hold down a steady job? Does he or she have the skills to cope with life?

Looking Back on the Teenage Years

During the teen years, both of our sons struggled terribly. As expected, my husband and I faced the typical teen challenges associated with AD/HD: poor school performance, forgetfulness with chores and homework, disorganization, losing things, messy rooms, disobedience, talking back, low frustration tolerance, lack of awareness of time and having a sleep disturbance.

School was always the major source of conflict with our sons. Both our boys did okay in elementary school. However, they fell apart in middle school when they had more classes and teachers, had greater academic demands placed on them and were expected to be more responsible and independent. Developmentally, they were not ready to complete their work independently.

> Fear and frustration were our constant companions and at times overwhelmed us.

Both boys struggled academically in middle and high school, and were in real danger of failing classes. Failure to complete homework or chores produced daily battles. The zeros for failure to turn in homework alternately baffled and infuriated us. It was not unusual to go into final exams with a passing grade hanging in the balance. Would they pass or fail? We didn't always know.

Emotionally charged conflicts were also common. Our children didn't always do as we asked. Obviously, their disobedience and our yelling battles were frustrating and a major source of embarrassment. As a result, we often harbored grave doubts about our own parenting skills. Fear and frustration were our constant companions and at times overwhelmed us. Our reactions ranged from anger and depression to verbal attacks upon our children.

Sleep problems were the underlying cause of ongoing fights before school each morning. I can't believe it took us so long to recognize that our son's **sleep disturbance**—difficulty falling asleep and waking up—was a serious handicap. Unfortunately, most treatment professionals never addressed this issue. But the problem is obvious: if a student is experiencing sleep deprivation, he or she cannot do well in school.

Behaviors that Worry Parents the Most

When our sons were teenagers we were frightened by some of their actions. In those days, we lacked basic information about the challenging behaviors teenagers with AD/HD often exhibit. Subsequently, Dr. Russell Barkley's research has been especially helpful. Awareness of these potential trouble spots often helps parents anticipate problem areas, implement preventive strategies, avoid being unnecessarily frightened and subsequently overreacting to misbehavior. Here are a few of the more serious behaviors about which we worried the most, along with brief tips from *Teenagers with ADD*.

Driving

Both our boys received more than their share of speeding tickets. Initially we were baffled by this behavior. At the time, we were not aware of Dr. Barkley's research that our teens are four times more likely to get speeding tickets than other drivers.

Tips:
- Send teenagers to driver training classes.
- Gradually increase driving privileges as they drive safely and without tickets.
- Talk with the doctor about taking medicine while driving during the early evening.

- Link driving privileges to responsible behavior, (e.g., for a child who is failing a class, try, "When you bring home a weekly report with all work completed, you will earn the privilege of driving to school the next week.") This gives parents greater leverage to influence behavior. Helpful tips are also available in
- *AD/HD and Driving* by Dr. Marlene Snyder.

Substance Use

Experimenting with substances is another area for parental concern. Children with AD/HD may be more likely to experiment with substances and tend to start at earlier ages. Substance experimentation may progress to abuse and eventually evolve into the more serious medical problem of addiction. The greatest risk for substance abuse is among children with more complex, coexisting conditions, e.g., AD/HD and conduct disorder or AD/HD and bipolar disorder. Several factors are often linked to substance abuse: 1) having friends who use substances, 2) being aggressive and hyperactive, 3) school failure, 4) low grades and 5) poor self-esteem.

Keep in mind, even if the teenager wants to stop using substances, he may not be able to take that step. Nagging will not help. Don't be judgmental or preachy. If your child is experiencing serious substance abuse problems, convey a sense of deep concern and help him find professional support.

Tips:
- Be aware of your child's friends and subtly influence his choice of companions as much as possible, e.g., "Would you like to invite John or Mark?"
- "Fine-tune" the treatment plan until serious aggression and hyperactivity are brought under control, (e.g., teach anger management or adjust medications for better results.)
- Educate yourself and your child about substances and signs of abuse.

- Avoid scare tactics.
- Provide supervision.
- Ensure success at school.

Suicide

Underneath their tough "I don't care" veneer, teenagers with AD/HD are often very sensitive and hide a lot of pain and hurtful life experiences. The *risk of a suicide attempt* is a very serious concern. One research study indicated that attempts occurred in between 5–10 percent of students with AD/HD. On a couple of occasions, we personally came face to face with the frightening knowledge that our sons were so depressed and their self-esteem so battered that they were at risk for a *suicide attempt*. One parent shared this personal story: "We could never quite see misbehavior the same after hearing our son say, 'I wish I could go to sleep and never wake up.' I sat up all night reassuring him we would work out whatever problems he faced. We were humbled, realizing that we needed to reevaluate our parenting styles."

Tips:
- Become familiar with the warning signs of suicide.
- **Take any threat to commit suicide seriously and seek professional help.**
- In the interim, listen to him talk about his concerns.
- Ask about suicidal thoughts. "Have you considered harming yourself?"
- Tell him how devastated you would be if anything happened to him.
- Remove potential weapons or dangerous medications from home.
- Keep him busy and provide supervision (engage in sports, movies or video games).

Trouble with the Law

Brushes with law enforcement are not uncommon. These children act impulsively, which may result in their being "invited" to juvenile court. If that happens in your family, don't

> Link driving privileges to responsible behavior.

overreact and assume that your child is going to be a delinquent. Obviously, brushes with the law often give parents a clear signal that the teenager is struggling and needs more guidance and supervision.

Tips:

♦ Be aware of the factors contributing to delinquency. "Deviant" friends who are breaking the law and abusing substances are influential factors. Here's a piece of interesting trivia: the peak time for juvenile crime is right after school.

♦ Keep your teenager busy after school or provide supervision. If necessary, hire a cook/housekeeper to keep an eye on things at home.

♦ Some parents may decide to work part-time so they can be home when their children are home.

♦ Identify the problem behaviors, implement an intervention strategy, and believe that you and your child will cope with the crisis.

Generally speaking, my husband and I were watchful of our sons' activities, tried to keep them busy with wholesome activities, knew who their friends were, knew where they were and with whom, provided inconspicuous supervision, offered our home as a place for teenage friends to congregate, and sought "win-win" compromises when they proposed unacceptable activities.

In spite of the challenges these children present, my view of the long-term outcome of adults with AD/HD is probably more positive than most people. AD/HD runs in my family and the people I know with this condition have been successful in their chosen careers. By sharing my family's experiences, both the good and bad, it is my goal to give you critical information about your teenager plus a sense of optimism that your family will cope successfully with AD/HD.

Like most parents of children with AD/HD, my husband and I were victims of a "code of silence" regarding our children's behavior. We thought we were the only family to experience these AD/HD behaviors and were too embarrassed to tell anyone about our children's failures and misbehavior. So we share this information with you now, in hopes that you will know that you are not alone on this journey. Because we have survived the ride, we can offer a sense of hope for a brighter future based upon our own firsthand experience.

References

Barkley, Russell A. (1998). *Attention deficit hyperactivity disorder.* New York: The Guilford Press.

Dendy, Chris A. Zeigler, (2000). *Teaching teens with ADD and ADHD* (Summary 28). Bethesda, Md: Woodbine House.

Dendy, Chris A. Zeigler, (1995). *Teenagers with ADD.* Bethesda, Md: Woodbine House.

Chris Dendy has over 30 years experience as a teacher, school psychologist, mental health counselor and administrator. Perhaps more importantly, she is the mother of two grown sons with AD/HD. Ms. Dendy is the author of two popular books on AD/HD and producer of two videotapes, Teen to Teen: the ADD Experience and Father to Father. She is also cofounder of Gwinnett County CHADD (GA) and has served on the national CHADD Board of Directors. She can be reached at chris@chrisdendy.com.

This article first appeared in *Attention!*® magazine, April 2002.

Finding the Joy—Parenting Teenagers with AD/HD (Part 2 of 2)

By Chris A. Zeigler Dendy, M.S.

In the previous article, we discussed the academic and behavioral challenges that so often accompany AD/HD. In addition, the typical teen challenges of achieving independence and more serious issues such as driving, drug use, suicide risk and brushes with the law were also reviewed, and several intervention strategies were suggested. Thankfully, the challenging teenage years are now behind our family. Our sons, Steven and Alex, are now 31 and 27, respectively, and have grown up to be responsible, productive adults. Steven is a college graduate, is married and the father of two children, owns his home, and has a wonderful management job in a manufacturing plant. Alex is only two courses shy of college graduation and is looking forward to a career in the criminal justice or computer fields. Early on we made a conscious decision to accept the fact that our boys might be on a six to eight-year college plan. In the overall scheme of a 70-year life-span, two or three extra years in college are not a big deal.

However, our lives have not always looked so rosy and optimistic. When our sons were in high school, my husband and I both had *serious* doubts whether or not they would graduate, let alone be successful in college. Fortunately, high school grades were not a good predictor of their performance in college. Although Steven struggled initially, he graduated from college making mostly A's and B's in his major classes. The same has been true for Alex; and they both have been on the Dean's list several times.

Reframing: Taking a Second Look at Strengths

Gratefully, the perception of "good and bad" behavior changes with the passage of time. Certain behaviors that are not endearing in children may be highly valued in adults. For example, although hyperactivity is not particularly desirable in school, high energy and the ability to work long hours at the office are valued. So, it is critically important for parents to learn to *reframe* or look at "negative" AD/HD behaviors in a positive way and share this philosophy with their child. In the following paragraphs, several examples are given for reframing some of our sons' so called, "negative AD/HD behaviors."

> It is critically important for parents to learn how to reframe or look at "negative" AD/HD behaviors in a positive way.

Our oldest son, **Steven**, with his classic *AD/HD combined type,* was a charming class clown. His teachers always loved him, and sometimes he could get away with saying or doing things because they liked him. Typically, if he got into trouble, he was able to talk them into giving milder consequences. These adaptive skills serve him well in his present job. Like many youngsters with AD/HD, he never meets a stranger. Customers find him personable and entertaining, and he also gets along well with the people he supervises.

Teen Drivers with AD/HD: Proceed with Caution

All parents struggle with the issues involved when their teens begin to drive, but there are additional issues that must be considered for the parents of teens with AD/HD. Official driving records show that individuals with AD/HD are involved in accidents about four times more often than those without the disorder, and are almost seven times more likely to be involved in two or more crashes*. Parents of teens with AD/HD can help reduce the risks of accidents if they:

- Make it clear that learning how to drive is a privilege the teen has to earn.
- Provide as much supervised driving time as possible with the child both before and after the child has obtained a license (frequent, short sessions are best).
- Determine with the child's physician whether medication is needed while the child drives; if so, ask the child to agree to consistent medication use while driving.
- Choose safe cars for driving, and retain ownership of the car the teen drives.
- Prohibit late-night driving, drinking and driving, and driving with other teens in the car; insist on seat belt use at all times.
- Consider using a driver's contract that specifically addresses the issues of teen drivers with AD/HD. Enforce consequences of poor driving performance and contract violations immediately.
- Agree on consequences for traffic tickets, accidents or violations of the agreed upon driving behavior. Be sure to follow through if and when these adverse driving events occur.

For more information, read *AD/HD & driving: A guide for parents of teens with AD/HD* by J. Marlene Snyder (Whitefish, MT: Whitefish Consultants, 2001).

*Barkley, R.; Murphy, K.; and Kwasnik, D. (1996). Vehicle driving competencies and risks in teens and young adults with attention deficit hyperactivity disorder. Pediatrics 98(6): 1089–1095.

During the teen years, Steven and his father engaged in loud, confrontational arguments. Steven could always hold his own since he is very verbal and expresses himself quite well. He is not intimidated by anyone, and is not afraid to give his opinions. Now, as an adult, we can appreciate these skills more fully. The days of loud arguments are long gone, Steven and his Dad love to fish together, and today my husband can truthfully say, "Steven is my best friend."

Steven also has a gift for working on mechanical things. He could repair just about anything on his car, and his pride in his car was obvious, since it was always spotlessly clean. Unfortunately, neither son had this same standard of cleanliness for their rooms or the garage. Now that they are older, their organization and cleanliness have improved.

Steven started college prior to the diagnosis of his AD/HD. And though he never failed a course, "he was invited to leave" after his first year because of his grades. Ultimately, this was a blessing in disguise. He went to work in a graphic arts company where he learned the basic skills necessary for working in a paperboard packaging company. At age 20, his AD/HD was finally diagnosed. He returned to college and took methylphenidate to help him study. His grades improved dramatically from D's to A's and B's.

After graduating, he accepted a management job with the company. He found a career that was a perfect match: a job that required constant activity, dealing with people, working with his hands, utilizing mechanical skills, and having a high energy level that allows him to easily work long hours.

Our second son, **Alex**, has *AD/HD/inattentive,* leaving us to deal with a different set of issues. He had serious learning problems that were never officially diagnosed and as a result, he struggled in school. Although intellectually gifted, he hated school and got through by the skin of his teeth. Unlike Steven, Alex was more reserved and distant from most of his teachers. Sometimes he couldn't even remember their names much less try to charm them.

Surprise! Surprise! Alex actually did better in college than he did in high school. We found that college faculty members were more flexible and accommodating than most of his high school teachers. Pursuant to Section 504, he received critical accommodations in classes and took a lighter load of 12 hours. He had untimed tests, early registration and pick of the teachers. He scheduled classes later in the morning to work around his sleep disturbance. Interestingly enough, college students actually spend fewer hours in class each week than high school students do—12 to 15 hours compared to 30.

Alex has always loved electronic gadgets. He loves operating them, taking them apart, but not always putting them back together. But this behavior ultimately produced a positive outcome: as he gets older, he is much better about putting them back together. And, as a result of his curiosity, he has learned a tremendous amount about electricity, electronics, electrical wiring and the operation of business machines.

Computer science and electronics are major strengths for Alex. He is a wizard working on his computer. He can repair it, rebuild it and program almost anything. If any of my business machines, phones or VCR breaks down, Alex is the one we call to repair it. Although he is majoring in criminal justice, his minor is in computer science.

Alex has also become quite proficient at home repair. After renting an apartment that looked like a bomb shelter, he spackled the holes in the ceiling and walls, installed a ceiling fan and air-conditioning unit, replaced the plumbing, and repaired the electrical wiring. I'm certain his grades suffered some, but he still passed everything, and what wonderful life skills he learned.

> Make a special effort to recognize and praise the child's strengths and successes.

Food For Thought

Most parents do the very best job they can raising their children, yet often worry that it isn't good enough. Consequently, Dr. Russell Barkley's comments provide some much needed reassurance, "The good news is that most parents of children with AD/HD are doing things right…typical parental mistakes are not irreparable or long lasting." Here are several parenting suggestions that my family has found effective:

♦ **Praise or reward good behavior and impose reasonable consequences for inappropriate behavior without obliterating the teen's self-esteem.**

♦ **Take charge and change the things you can.** Actions that parents can take to influence a child's successful outcome include: seeking accommodations at school to ensure academic success, fine-tuning medication, using positive parenting practices, providing supervision, avoiding hostile interactions and harsh punishment, avoiding nagging and personal attacks, and last and perhaps most importantly, believing in your child!

♦ **Consequences should be instructive, not just punitive!** Teach your child skills or how to compensate for his deficits, rather than simply punishing him for lacking those essential life skills.

- **Be positive. Reframe AD/HD behaviors!** Parents must continually monitor their negative thoughts, comments and actions and make a special effort to recognize and praise the child's strengths and successes. View the "cup as half full rather than half empty." Take a closer second look at AD/HD behaviors to find and nurture their positive elements.

- **Stay centered and steady in your belief in your child's ultimate success!** Parents may see their teenager struggling at school, having conflicts with authority figures or perhaps even having a few brushes with law enforcement. As a result, the family is often bombarded with negative messages from a variety of sources: the school, counselors, doctors or the juvenile court system. We hear the classic lines: "He could do it if he would only try. You've got to punish him. He has to be responsible for his actions."

A positive self-fulfilling philosophy is very powerful: if you convey by word and action that you expect your teenager to be responsible, he will usually rise to your expectations. In other words, if parents believe their teenager is "good" and will succeed in life, then he probably will. Unfortunately, the opposite is also true. If parents think their teenager is "bad" and treat him that way, the teenager will have greater difficulty succeeding.

- **Treat your teenager as a partner and involve him in the problem-solving process.** Empower teenagers, treat them with respect, listen to them and address their concerns.

- **Listen to your teenager!** For example, if medication refusal is a problem, you may find—if you ask—that they are too embarrassed to go to the office to take it.

- **"Keep a disability perspective"**— excellent advice given by Dr. Russell Barkley! For some of these children, *AD/HD is truly a disability.* I frequently have to remind myself of these words of wisdom. The invisible nature of AD/HD as a disability makes it so easy to assume that the child could do the task if he would just try. A child with diabetes would not be blamed or punished for his inability to regulate blood sugar levels. Similarly, *children with AD/HD can't regulate the level of their neurotransmitters and should not just be punished for their "AD/HD behaviors."*

- **Remember that "AD/HD behaviors" are part of the condition; not malicious misbehavior!** Because of their *two-to four-year developmental lag,* they may act less mature and assume less responsibility. Because they are *impulsive,* they don't always think of the consequences before they act or speak. Because they

are *forgetful and disorganized,* they may forget chores or assignments, lose things or have a bedroom that is a wreck. Because of their *impaired sense of time,* they are going to be late. Because of *their sleep disturbances,* they have trouble falling asleep or may be extremely difficult to wake up. Because they *don't learn from punishment and reward* as easily as other children, they will be more difficult to discipline and may repeat misbehavior.

♦ **If you can't change the "AD/HD behavior," change the environment.** Buy your tardy child a wrist watch alarm or beep him when he is due home.

♦ **Use depersonalization.** Try saying, "Teenagers with AD/HD often have trouble remembering their homework assignments. Sometimes this seems to be true for you. How can I help you solve this problem?"

♦ **Give choices.** Teenagers who are given choices are more compliant, less aggressive and produce more school work. "Do you want to start homework at 7:00 or 7:30?"

♦ **Teach skills.** Teach time management, social skills, study skills or anger management. *Sometimes we forget that AD/HD is no picnic for our children!* They did not ask to have this disorder. An eight-year-old child prayed, "Dear God, please don't let me have AD/HD." A teenager cried, "Am I going to feel this way all my life? I feel like I am going to die of anxiety."

Although parenting these children is often more difficult, requires more energy, and takes longer than for other children, don't give up. Continue to *believe in yourself and in your teenager!* Hopefully, you will be as lucky as my husband and I: as young adults, our sons are our best friends.

Please spend a few minutes now and *take a second look at teenagers from a fresh vantage point.* What are their strengths and special talents? Involve them as partners who, with your love and support, will try their best to cope successfully with this challenge called AD/HD!

References

Barkley, Russell A. (1998). *Attention deficit hyperactivity disorder.* New York: The Guilford Press.

Brown, Thomas E. (2000). *Attention deficit disorders and comorbidities in children, adolescents, and adults.* Washington, DC: American Psychiatric Press.

Dendy, Chris A. Zeigler. (1995). *Teenagers with ADD.* Bethesda, MD: Woodbine House.

Chris A. Zeigler Dendy, M.S., has over 30 years experience as a teacher, school psychologist, mental health counselor and administrator. More importantly, she is the mother of two grown sons with AD/HD. Ms. Dendy is the author of two popular books on AD/HD and producer of two videotapes, Teen to Teen: the ADD Experience and Father to Father. She is also cofounder of the Gwinnett County CHADD (Ga) and a past member of CHADD's Board of Directors. For more information, visit her Web site at www.chrisdendy.com.

This article first appeared in *Attention!®* magazine, June 2002.

Teens with AD/HD: Transitions from High School to College or Career

by Edward M. Gotlieb, M.D., FAAP, FSAM

For the recent high school graduate, figuring out what to do next can be confusing. Add attention-deficit/hyperactivity disorder (AD/HD) to the mix, and the issues become even more complex. Fortunately, recent research and the clinical experiences of physicians who treat teens with AD/HD offer help for those preparing to transition to college or work. What follows are several ideas for teens and their families to ensure success as the student transitions from high school to the next stage in life.

Plan Ahead

As a person with AD/HD, you are entitled to reasonable accommodations for standardized tests, which are typically required for admittance to college. For example, both the SAT and ACT organizations can arrange for testing under special circumstances if your medical situation warrants it. For young people with AD/HD, extended time for testing is often requested and, with proper documentation, granted. Examination results are not marked as being any different from standard testing. However, it is important to begin the process soon enough to get the proper approvals. A good place to start is with your school's guidance counselor. You will need documentation of your need for special arrangements from your health professional. You will need time for them to generate a report and for the testing board to review and approve accommodations. In short: start early.

If your intent is to enter the military, you also need to do some research. The regulations about whether students with AD/HD can enlist vary with the military's needs and seem to change fairly frequently. Your acceptance may even depend on an individual recruiter's understanding of your situation. Currently, a person must be off all medication for any behavioral disorder for at least one year before any of the services will consider him or her as a recruit. No accommodations for testing to qualify for enlistment are allowed. The NRC has a summary of the current requirements on its Web site,[1] (www.help4adhd.org).

Talking to a military recruiter early in the process can also be a way to learn more.

Get Your Medical Care Squared Away

It is often harder to get insurance and medical care after leaving high school. Parental health policies may not provide adequate coverage. Federal and state-supported programs, including Medicaid, State Children's Health Insurance Program (SCHIP) and Supplemental Security Income (SSI), may end once you become 18 years old.[2] The average medical costs incurred by patients with AD/HD are about twice those of patients without the disorder.[3]

Having proper medical support and funds to cover care is important for anyone transitioning out of high school. Since individuals with AD/HD benefit from careful monitoring of their condition, medication treatment and sophisticated medical knowledge, making proper arrangements is essential.

It also may be harder for you to find adequate adult-oriented medical care.[4] Pediatricians may not be comfortable taking care of young adult patients or may have limitations in their ability to admit these patients to children's hospitals. Family practitioners, internists and gynecologists may feel uncomfortable dealing with the problems of the young adult with a chronic condition. Psychiatrists are generally not in a position to handle primary health care needs. Student health services are rarely available all day, every day, particularly during school vacations. Again, it is helpful to start early. Recent work by J.G. Reiss and colleagues emphasizes the benefit of beginning work with your current physician "envisioning a future" and preparing for a transition into the adult-oriented health care system.[5]

Know Yourself

When young adults begin preparing for college or work after high school, many wonder if they can handle their AD/HD without medication. For the majority of those who have successfully responded to medication, however, continuing medical treatment is clearly the best course of action. College and work both require more self-discipline than high school. This is not the best time to change any more variables than necessary, particularly if you move out of your family home. Remember that people with AD/HD have more traffic accidents and a higher lifetime risk of drug and alcohol abuse than people without the disorder. Medication treatment lowers both of these risks.

Regardless of your medication decision, you need to look at your strengths and weaknesses in dealing with new social settings and time management. Are you more comfortable in a smaller school where there is more individual attention or in a larger school where there may be greater opportunities for finding more varied activities and a wider range of classmates? Would you be better off staying at home, staying in the community or starting over in a new environment? Does the support network of a fraternity or sorority seem like a benefit or a distraction?[6]

If you are going to enter the job market, many of the same questions arise: a larger organization may have more formal structures and support programs available. A smaller work setting may (or may not) be able to accommodate your specific needs for training and modifications in your work environment. It makes sense to ask about such details and conditions before you commit to the work site.

Use Resources

Make early contact with your college's special services department.[7] By registering, you can gain access to knowledgeable professionals and

> The regulations about whether students with AD/HD can enlist vary with the military's needs and seem to change fairly frequently.

> To enter the workplace, make your best effort to get some early exposure in an area that interests you.

helpful arrangements, such as a late drop date for courses that become too much to handle.

To enter the workplace, make your best effort to get some early exposure in an area that interests you. Accepting volunteer work rather than a paying position is a good way to see what the field is like. You also will have a chance to connect with others who already work in a given field to find out whether such work is right for you. If you later decide to go back to school, such volunteer experience may get you a closer look by the admissions staff.

Take Your Time

In high school, you may feel a strong pressure to graduate with your class. In college, there is less focus on this issue since most classes are open to a wider group of students who are there because of their specific interests, requirements and level of training. This situation is ideal for you as an individual with AD/HD because it can allow you to progress at your own speed and control the amount and complexity of the work.

Remember: moving beyond high school can be fun and exciting if you prepare carefully for what lies ahead.

Notes

1. National Resource Center on AD/HD. (2004). *AD/HD and the Military.* Available at http://www.help4adhd.org/living/work-place/military, accessed on 3/6/05.
2. Newacheck, P.W., Park, M.J., Brindis, C.D., Biehl, M. & Irwin, C.E. (2004). Trends in private and public health insurance for adolescents. (March 2004). *Journal of the American Medical Association, 291*(10):1231–7.
3. Leibson, C.L., Katusic, S.K., Barbaresi, W.J., Ransom, J. & O'Brien, P.C. (2001). Use and costs of medical care for children and adolescents with and without attention-deficit/hyperactivity disorder. *Journal of the American Medical Association, 285*(1): 60–6.
4. Blum, R.W., Editor. (2002). *Improving Transitions for Adolescents with Special Health Care Needs from Pediatric to Adult-Centered Health Care. Pediatrics, 110*(6) Supplement.
5. Reiss, J.G., Gibson, R.W. & Walker, L.R. (2005). Health care transition: Youth, family and provider perspectives. *Pediatrics, 115:* 112–120.
6. Dendy, C.A.Z. (1995). *Teenagers with ADD: A Parents' Guide.* Bethesda, Md.: Woodbine House, 287–313.
7. Bramer, J.S. (1996). *Succeeding in College with Attention Deficit Disorders.* Plantation, Fl.: Specialty Press, Inc.

Edward M. Gotlieb M.D., FAAP, FSAM, is a practicing pediatrician and the medical director of the Pediatric Center, Stone Mountain, Ga. He is a member of the American Academy of Pediatrics Work Group on Adolescents with AD/HD.

Editor's Note: The National Resource Center on AD/HD (NRC) has developed several sheets on topics most relevant to adults with AD/HD, including "College Issues for Students with AD/HD" and "Guidelines for Succeeding in the Workplace with AD/HD." These materials can be accessed at www.help4adhd.org/en/about.

This article first appeared in *Attention!*® magazine, June 2005.

When AD/HD and Substance Abuse Collide

by Timothy E. Wilens, M.D.

Within the past few years, there has been increasing interest in the overlap of attention-deficit/hyperactivity disorder (AD/HD) and addictive disorders. The combination of AD/HD and substance abuse (including drug and alcohol abuse and dependence) has been frequently reported and is known to be associated with substantial impairment. While AD/HD emerges in early childhood and affects 3–5 percent of school-aged children and approximately 2–4 percent of adults, the substance use disorders tend to begin in adolescence or early adulthood and affect 25 percent of adults. Both substance abuse and AD/HD are related by their relationship to the neurotransmitter dopamine.

Cigarette smoking rates are almost double in adolescents with AD/HD. Studies have shown that approximately one-third of the children growing up with AD/HD will have a problem with substance abuse. Children with AD/HD who have ongoing problems with their AD/HD (including prominent attention problems) as well as demoralization were shown in these studies to be at higher risk for substance abuse. The co-occurrence of conduct disorder (delinquency) and bipolar disorder greatly increase the chance that a child with AD/HD will have problems with teenage-onset substance use problems.

A number of accumulating studies have shown elevated rates of substance abuse in adults with AD/HD as compared to the general population. More specifically, in a group of adults with AD/HD approximately one-third have had alcohol abuse or dependence histories, while approximately one-fifth have had drug abuse or dependence histories. In addition, a recent study at Massachusetts General Hospital indicates that most of the adults with AD/HD and substance abuse issues (generally alcohol or marijuana) also had problems with mood, anxiety or an antisocial condition.

Not surprisingly, studies in adolescents and adults with an addiction indicate an over-representation of AD/HD. Including both alcohol and drug addiction, approximately 40 percent of adolescents and 20 percent of adults with substance abuse have AD/HD. For example, Howard Schubiner, M.D., and colleagues found that 24 percent of 201 inpatients in a substance abuse treatment facility had AD/HD. The importance of careful diagnosis, however, has been demonstrated by Frances Rudnick Levin, M.D., and colleagues who found that while 10 percent of adults who were cocaine dependent met strict criteria for AD/HD (clear childhood and adult AD/HD), another 11 percent were found to have AD/HD symptoms only as adults that may have represented cocaine-induced brain

> Approximately one-third of the children growing up with AD/HD will have a problem with substance abuse.

dysfunction. Adults with addictions who have AD/HD typically have a more severe course of the addiction and difficulties in recovery.

It appears that children with AD/HD, coupled with other conditions such as conduct disorder, are at risk for very early cigarette smoking and substance use disorder as adolescents, whereas individuals with AD/HD alone are at risk as young adults—age 18–21. Of interest, girls with AD/HD may start using and misusing substances at an earlier age than boys.

Both family/genetic and psychological issues are probably operational in causing substance abuse in individuals with AD/HD. Elevated rates of substance abuse have been found in the relatives of children and adults with AD/HD, and elevated rates of AD/HD have been reported in the relatives of individuals with substance abuse.

Adults or adolescents with AD/HD do not abuse a specific type of drug, for example cocaine. Instead, availability of drugs and alcohol appears to be the most important determining factor. Like adolescents and adults who do not have AD/HD and who abuse substances, individuals with AD/HD most frequently abuse marijuana. Marijuana is probably the most misused substance, in part because of its easy availability in the community. Yet, why individuals use substances may shed light on some self-medication behaviors. For example, my colleagues and I recently found that adolescents and young adults with AD/HD were more likely to initiate and continue substances to alter their mood and to help them get to sleep than did kids without AD/HD.

Treatment considerations

Evaluation and treatment of co-occurring AD/HD and substance abuse should be part of a plan in which consideration is given to all aspects of the individual's life (see sidebar, page 19). Any intervention in this group should follow a careful evaluation of the individual and his or her family including addic-

tion, psychiatric, social, cognitive and, if applicable, educational evaluations. A thorough history of substance use should be obtained in all individuals with AD/HD including past and current usage. Careful attention should be paid to the other problems that may exist, including medical or neurological conditions whose symptoms may be similar to those of AD/HD. Although no specific guidelines exist for evaluating the individual who is an active substance abuser, in our experience, at least one month of abstinence is helpful in assessing current AD/HD symptoms. Careful psychiatric assessments by a professional knowledgeable in both addiction and AD/HD is suggested.

When treating individuals with AD/HD and active substance abuse, special attention should be given to other potential psychological and cognitive disorders. The presence of depression or anxiety that is not directly a result of the substance abuse needs to be further assessed. The overall evaluation should assist in the designing of a multimodal treatment plan tailored to the needs of the individual. Multimodal treatment includes parent and child education about diagnosis and treatment, behavior management techniques, medication and school programming and supports.

The treatment of individuals with active substance abuse and AD/HD needs to be addressed simultaneously with an initial emphasis on the substance abuse. It is noteworthy that AD/HD treatments should not be relied upon to correct the behavioral patterns of substance abuse. In fact, the bulk of research data indicates that AD/HD treatment does not treat substance use issues adequately in adolescents or adults with AD/HD who abuse substances. Additionally, these individuals often suffer from poor self-esteem, high risk-taking behaviors and difficulty sitting through 12-step programs and individual or group psychotherapy. Effective psychotherapy for individuals with AD/HD and substance abuse generally combines structured and goal-directed sessions, active therapist involvement and frequent reassessments. Substance abuse and AD/HD psychotherapies can be completed successfully in parallel with other addiction therapeutic methods (i.e., Narcotics Anonymous) and pharmacotherapy.

Pharmacotherapy serves an important role in reducing the core symptoms of AD/HD and other concurrent psychiatric disorders and, therefore, may indirectly assist in substance abuse treatment. The pharmacological treatments for AD/HD, such as stimulants and non-stimulants, do not make substance use worse; yet immediate-release stimulants may be misused or sold by substance abusers. Favorable reports of medication treatment for adolescents and adults with AD/HD and substance abuse disorder (SUD) have included the use of stimulants and bupropion. Atomoxetine, an agent without abuse potential, is very intriguing but remains untested in this group.

When using drug therapy, frequent monitoring should include careful evaluation of treatment compliance, substance use status (random toxicology screens) and coordination of care with caregivers. In adolescents and adults with AD/HD who have histories of substance abuse but are now clean or sober, there is no data indicating that nonstimulants or stimulants will put them at risk for relapse. In contrast, AD/HD treatment may assist in preventing relapses while improving the adolescent's or adult's likelihood for general life success.

Addressing the Myths and Concerns

Over the last decade, reports of illicit use of stimulant medications have emerged. A survey study completed in Wisconsin indicated that 16 percent of children had been approached to sell or give away their medication. Along the same lines, a more recent survey study completed in Nova Scotia in junior and senior high school students indicated that 15 percent had given their medications to others while 7 percent had sold their medication to other students. Similarly, reports of diversion in college-

aged youth are emerging. For example, we recently found that 11 percent of a sample of 21-year-olds with AD/HD were selling their medication. Those selling their medication also had substance abuse problems. Moreover, despite the availability of extended-release stimulants (e.g., Concerta, Adderall XR, Ritalin LA, Metadate CD), only immediate-release medications were diverted. The lessons to be learned: parents must supervise the storage of adolescents' medications, and college students should be advised to safely store their medications (not in medicine cabinets), and physicians should utilize extended-release stimulants in this age group.

Do the stimulant medications used to treat AD/HD actually lead to substance abuse? Although concerns have been raised that early stimulant exposure may lead individuals to substance abuse in general and to specific substances, such as cocaine, clinical studies do not appear to support this belief. The results of a recent study indicate that the use of stimulant medication reduces the risk to start smoking cigarettes. Likewise, results from an analysis of seven worldwide studies found that stimulant pharmacotherapy did not increase the risk for later substance abuse. In fact, individuals with AD/HD being treated with stimulants had lower rates of SUD. It may be that the ultimate risk of substance abuse in treated individuals with AD/HD may approximate the risk in individuals without AD/HD (the general population).

In summary, there is a large body of literature supporting a relationship between AD/HD and substance abuse. Complex genetic, behavioral and self-medication influences contribute to the development and persistence of substance abuse in those with AD/HD. Treating AD/HD reduces the risk for cigarette

> The use of stimulant medication reduces the risk to start smoking cigarettes.

smoking and substance abuse. Individuals with AD/HD and current substance abuse require comprehensive multimodal intervention incorporating parallel addiction and mental health treatment.

References

Biederman, J., Faraone, S.V., Spencer, T., Wilens, T.E., Norman, D., Lapey, K.A., et al. (1993). Patterns of psychiatric comorbidity, cognition, and psychosocial functioning in adults with attention deficit hyperactivity disorder. *American Journal of Psychiatry, 150*:1792–1798.

Biederman, J., Wilens, T., Mick, E., Faraone, S., Weber, W., Curtis, S., et al. (1997). Is ADHD a risk for psychoactive substance use disorder? Findings from a four year follow-up study. *Journal of the American Academy of Child and Adolescent Psychiatry, 36*:21–29.

Grabowski, J., Shearer, J., Merrill, J. & Negus, S.S. (2004). Agonist-like, replacement pharmacotherapy for stimulant abuse and dependence. *Addictive Behaviors, 29*:1439–1464.

Levin, F.R., Evans, S. & Kleber, H.D. (1998). Prevalence of adult attention-deficit/hyperactivity disorder among cocaine abusers seeking treatment. *Drug and Alcohol Dependence, 52*:15–25.

Molina, B. & Pelham, W. (2003). Childhood predictors of adolescent substance use in a longitudinal study of children with ADHD. *Journal of Abnormal Psychology, 112*(3): 497–507.

Musser, C., Ahmann, P., Theye, F.W., Mundt, P., Broste, S. & Mueller-Rizner, N. (1998). Stimulant use and potential for abuse in Wisconsin as reported by school administrators and longitudinally followed children. *Developmental and Behavioral Pediatrics, 19*:187–192.

Poulin, C. (2001). Medical and nonmedical stimulant use among adolescents: From sanctioned to unsanctioned use. *Canadian Medical Association Journal, 165*:1039–1044.

Riggs, P. (2003). Treating adolescents for substance abuse and comorbid psychiatric disorders. *Science & Practice Perspectives, 2*:18–28.

Schubiner, H., Tzelepis, A., Milberger, S., Lockhart, N., Kruger, M., Kelley, B.J., et al. (2000). Prevalence of attention-deficit/hyperactivity disorder and conduct disorder among substance abusers. *Journal of Clinical Psychiatry, 61*:244–251.

Vitiello, B. (2001). Long-term effects of stimulant medications on the brain: Possible relevance to the treatment of attention deficit hyperactivity disorder. *Journal of Child and Adolescent Psychopharmacology, 11*:25–34.

Wilens, T. (2004). Attention-deficit/hyperactivity disorder and the substance use disorders: The nature of the relationship, subtypes at risk and treatment issues. In T. Spencer (Ed.), *Psychiatric Clinics of North America, 27*: 283–302. Philadelphia: Saunders Press.

Wilens, T., Faraone, S., Biederman, J. & Gunawardene, S. (2003). Does stimulant therapy of ADHD beget later substance abuse: A metanalytic review of the literature. *Pediatrics, 11*:179–185.

Timothy E. Wilens, M.D., is an associate professor of psychiatry at Harvard Medical School in Boston, Mass. He is also director of the Substance Abuse Services in the Pediatric Psychopharmacology Clinic at Massachusetts General Hospital. Dr. Wilens' research interests include the relationship of attention-deficit/hyperactivity disorder (AD/HD), bipolar disorder and substance abuse; the pharmacotherapy of AD/HD across the lifespan; and juvenile bipolar disorder. Dr. Wilens has served on CHADD's Professional Advisory Board.

This article first appeared in *Attention!*® magazine, December 2004.

College Success: Accommodations and Strategies that Work

by Lynda J. Katz, Ph.D.

Asuccessful college experience for a student with AD/HD depends on identifying the particular problems that might arise due to unique learning styles and needs. Success also depends on overcoming the obstacles that often arise due to AD/HD symptoms, including:

- The desire for independence or wanting to go it alone
- Problems with working memory functions
- Difficulty sustaining attention and concentration over long periods
- Impairments in executive function
- Co-existing conditions (i.e., oppositional defiant disorder, learning disabilities, bipolar, etc.)

Wanting to go it alone

Feeling stigmatized is common for many students who have been diagnosed with AD/HD or a learning disability, leading many to shy away from seeking help in favor of coming up with their own remedies.

It is important for people to seek and receive appropriate accommodations. Furthermore, unless the diagnosis of AD/HD or a learning disorder is formally documented, with current recommendations for accommodations, and officially on file with the learning or disability services office, no additional support services will be provided at the college level.

Working memory

Working memory functions refer to processes involved in the encoding of information, categorizing it through a logical filing system for later retrieval and holding the information in temporary storage while the filing process takes place. These functions are often most impacted by underlying AD/HD. Understanding how working memory affects the learning process is essential for self-understanding, but is often misunderstood by students with AD/HD.

This is unfortunate, as college learning typically places great demands on working memory. Rote memory, once highly effective in the elementary school years and to some extent later in middle school and early high school, is no longer an effective learning strategy. Scanning texts and recalling just enough information to pass tests no longer works because too many of the salient details are missed in the scanning process. These important details serve as the building blocks for more advanced course work, and if they are missed, learning is further impeded.

Sustaining attention and concentration

Understanding AD/HD as a dysfunction of the attention system is also important. There are students whose error rate on exams is intensified because of impulsive response patterns, such as having a difficult time staying with a subject or reading passage that is not perceived as "interesting." Students who have hyperactive tendencies often find it difficult to stay with a long multi-hour examination without drifting off. Others vacillate between hyperfocusing and being distracted by everything going on around them.

Impairments in executive functions

In addition to working memory, other executive functions important for academic success involve time management, organization and planning, prioritizing, activation, arousal and effort. These aspects of executive function can also be problematic for students with AD/HD because of the unstructured nature of the college environment, an environment that does not readily reinforce this internal executive function system.

Parents have often served the role of "external executive functioner" for their children, providing external cues and supports in order to help the student meet deadlines and manage his or her time effectively. Without those external parental supports, students will need to explicitly identify other means to successfully get to class on time (for example, several alarm clocks strategically placed in the dorm room, timing of medication, personal digital assistants, etc.), to follow through with and complete homework and prioritize long-term assignments.

Students often mention difficulty getting started on a homework assignment. With the freedom and choice that the college environment provides, problems with activation are intensified, as distractions become rationalizations for not beginning homework or other long-term projects. Getting access early on to an advisor/coach who can support the gradual internalization of these aspects of executive function, as well as the appropriate use of medication, may be critical to the success of the student making the adjustment to the college setting.

> Getting access early on to an advisor/coach may be critical to the success of the student making the adjustment to the college setting.

Co-existing conditions

Finally, it is important to recognize that some 20–25 percent of students with AD/HD at the college level will also have a specific learning disorder (Semrud-Clikeman et al., 1992). A significant number may also have other diagnostic conditions such as an anxiety disorder, depression, substance abuse and sleep disorder found typically in adult populations with AD/HD (Biederman et al., 1993). Understanding the impact of such co-existing conditions on memory and learning functions as well as interpersonal and social relations are also factors that need to be considered when talking about successful adjustment at the college level.

Accommodations

Any request for accommodation must meet both the Americans with Disabilities Act (ADA) and Section 504 standards and be justified in a psychoeducational or neuropsychological report using the guidelines established and recommended for use by the Consortium on AD/HD Documentation (1998). It is important for students to understand the specific accommodations they will need. Not all students with AD/HD benefit from identical modifications nor do they use them in the same way or to the same degree (Richard, 1995). The guidelines have been adopted by the Educational Testing Service (ETS) as their Policy Statement for Documentation of Attention-Deficit/Hyperactivity Disorder in Adolescents and Adults. The policy is available through their Web site at www.ets.org.

Accommodations must be individualized to the needs of the particular student. There is no "one size fits all" approach or recipe to follow with respect to reasonable accommodations. A list of possible accommodations might include:

♦ Extended time for examinations
♦ Examinations to be provided in a non-distracting environment

- Use of a computer with spell and grammar check for all essay examinations and those having a short-answer format
- Access to a writing center for assistance with proofing final drafts of papers
- Access to a calculator for all math classes and examinations
- Access to a note taker for large lecture-based classes
- Ability to choose class times that facilitate the learning process
- Access to assistive technologies such as text-to-speech software programs, cognitive mapping programs and those with speech dictation capabilities
- A waiver for foreign language study
- Access to a quiet space for study
- Access to a coaching center or advisor/mentor

Learning Strategies

In addition to the accommodations discussed previously, there are a number of specific learning strategies that the individual student can take upon himself to institute. In some cases, he or she may need some specific instruction in how to undertake these, as they have never been a part of his or her skill sets. Many colleges will offer summer courses for high school juniors and seniors that deal with specific study skills and techniques. They teach strategies for handling reading assignments, written reports, essays and math classes.

Reading and listening. College texts used in the natural and social science, as well as those used in the humanities, require a high level of cognitive processing. In order to achieve that processing most efficiently, it is helpful to apply a consistent strategy across subject matters. Specific study skills and strategies become the building blocks for this

"metacognitive" approach to learning and its transferability across subject specific content. These include:

- Active reading
- Highlighting
- Making margin notes
- Identifying new vocabulary
- Making summary statements
- Note taking
- Using two column paper with all discrete notes in the right column
- Reviewing notes and then applying main ideas or headings in the left column

Study skills manuals also suggest prereading as a strategy (identifying major headings or sections in the chapter prior to in-depth reading). While this often works for science texts, it is less useful with humanities texts. Also, students who typically skim the material may miss crucial details. Finally, tackling the most difficult reading materials when one's mind is the

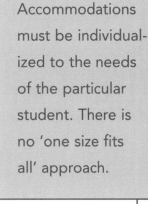

Accommodations must be individualized to the needs of the particular student. There is no 'one size fits all' approach.

What about Medication Management?

While medication management is not necessarily a reasonable accommodation or a learning strategy, it is often a critical factor in the initial adjustment to college life for many students with AD/HD. The following suggestions address student and parent concerns in this area.

If a student has a physician at home who currently manages his or her medications, that physician can call in a prescription to the local pharmacy where the college or university is located. The phone call must be followed by a paper copy of the prescription. It is a good idea for the paper copy prescription to be post-dated, as mail may take as long as four or five days to reach the pharmacy. This is important because, in some states, prescriptions for scheduled drugs will be honored only for a certain number of days. In Vermont, for example, there is a seven-day limit on prescriptions for scheduled drugs (the class into which psychostimulants such as Ritalin, Concerta and Adderall fall).

Some insurance companies only cover medication costs if the prescription is filled in the state in which the student permanently resides. In this case, it might be helpful to call the college's health services prior to enrollment for assistance in finding a local physician and/or psychiatrist to manage the medications.

One of the other major problems that occurs for college students is remembering to renew a prescription. Let's say that the student is down to his or her last pill, and no prescription is at hand. In this case, students should give the name and phone number of their home physician to the campus health service. Oftentimes, the health service will place the call to the physician and, as a temporary measure, fill a one-month prescription until the official refill prescription has been received. Obviously, this is a last resort and one that cannot be abused.

Finally, colleges generally offer student health insurance coverage as part of student services. It is important to check ahead of time to see whether the college's student health insurance covers prescriptions including psychostimulants. If it does, then problems with out-of-state insurance coverage can be alleviated.

freshest makes the most sense. Taking part regularly and consistently in some form of physical exercise or activity after a day of classes helps to refresh the attention system for later study hours.

Listening to lectures in large auditorium-like classrooms is often the rule vs. the exception for introductory freshman courses at many universities.

Being able to take notes in a consistent and meaningful way will be critical to later retention. If the student's handwriting is illegible, then taking notes with a pen or pencil is essentially useless. Using a laptop computer for this purpose is far more efficient and effective as long as the student has the necessary keyboarding skills or facility. Students with AD/HD may find that distractibility and hyperactivity can be major barriers in large classrooms. Getting access to a fellow student's notes for comparison purposes or reviewing one's own notes with the faculty member or classroom assistant during office hours can pay off.

Writing

Visual mapping or dictation software can be extremely useful for those students who have problems with transitional sentences or phrases or who have problems with the logical sequencing of ideas.

Computers are wonderful for students with AD/HD; however, some students can delete whole sections in an attempt to make everything perfect and have nothing to show after several hours of work. Using a writing center to help support the initial formulation of ideas into written notes may be helpful. Learning how to brainstorm ideas without self-censorship can be a very liberating experience. Receiving reinforcement from a writing coach or peer tutor for sections of a written paper rather than getting feedback on the entire draft may prove to be useful as well.

Making the Most of AD/HD

It has been my experience that students with AD/HD are some of the brightest, most creative and best thinkers in our classrooms today. But it takes effort to help them make creative ideas become concrete realities. I have a son-in-law, a highly successful surgeon, who also has AD/HD. In high school he played football and marched with the band during halftime. Now he can work on four journal articles at the same time, take breaks to watch TV, spend time with his 15-month-old son, talk with his buddy and then run to the Home Depot to get porch furniture, which he puts together with the ease of a skilled mechanic. During a two-week break in his fourth year of medical school, he built an office for me. At one point in his early medical school days, this young man doubted his ability to succeed because he had AD/HD. He would not tell you that today; he has learned to use his gifts with positive results, leaving the rest of us to catch up.

References

Biederman, J., Faraone, S.V., Spencer, T., et al. (1993). Patterns of psychiatric comorbidity, cognition and psychosocial functioning in adults with attention-deficit/hyperactivity disorder. *American Journal of Psychiatry, 150:*1792–1798.

Educational Testing Service. (1998). *Policy Statement for Documentation of Attention-Deficit/Hyperactivity Disorder in Adolescents and Adults.* Office of Disability Policy Educational Testing Service. Princeton, NJ.

Richard, M.M. (1995). Pathways to success for the college student with ADD accommodations and preferred practices. *Journal of Postsecondary Education and Disability, 11:* 16–30.

Semrud-Clikeman, M., Biederman, J., Sprich-Buckminster, S., et al. (1992). Comorbidity between ADHD and learning disability: A review and report in a clinically referred sample. *Journal of American Academy of Child Adolescent Psychiatry, 31:*439–448.

Author's Note: Special thanks to Simonne Holton, FNP, director of Student Health Services at Landmark College, Putney, Vt., for her input regarding medication management issues.

Lynda J. Katz, Ph.D., has been president of Landmark College, the nation's leading college for students with learning disabilities and AD/HD, since 1994. Prior to that, she served for more than 20 years on the faculty of the University of Pittsburgh School of Medicine, Department of Psychiatry, holding joint appointments with the Schools of Education and Health and Rehabilitation Sciences. Dr. Katz has served on CHADD's Professional Advisory Board.

This article first appeared in *Attention!*® magazine, August 2004.

Workplace Giving through CFC, United Way and Other Appeals Supports CHADD's Mission

A workplace payroll-giving pledge or direct gift to CHADD through the United Way, the Combined Federal Campaign (CFC) or other employee deduction program is an excellent way to support CHADD's work on behalf of people and families impacted by attention-deficit/hyperactivity disorder (AD/HD).

The enrollment period of CFC - like many United Way, corporate, state, municipal and corporate campaigns - begins in early September and runs through November. Please remember to use CHADD's CFC No. 2555 when enrolling for the Combined Federal Campaign, which is for federal civilian employees, the U.S. Postal Service and members of the Armed Forces. For United Way and other workplace programs, in most cases, you will have to write CHADD in on the campaign pledge cards. The mailing address is: 8181 Professional Place, Suite 150, Landover, MD 20785, (301) 306-7070, ext. 110.

CHADD is an IRS-approved, non-profit, tax-exempt Section 501 (c) (3) charity and donations are tax-deductible to the full extent of the law. For further information, please contact the CHADD Development Department.

Support CHADD's Mission to improve the lives of people affected by AD/HD through Collaborative leadership, Advocacy, Research, Education and Support – CHADD CARES!

CHADD®
CHILDREN AND ADULTS WITH
ATTENTION-DEFICIT/HYPERACTIVITY DISORDER

CFC
Combined Federal Campaign

#2555

Chapter 5
AD/HD in Adults

Poor Self-Control and How It Impacts Relationships

by Phyllis Anne Teeter Ellison, Ed.D., and Sam Goldstein, Ph.D.

At work I am animated when expressing my views on issues during meetings. My colleagues think I am angry and intimidating. It doesn't feel that way to me. I see myself as passionate and engaged in lively discussion or debate. Why do I feel like people don't understand me and are misreading my emotions? Am I too intense or are they stoic and disengaged? What am I missing? At parties I often say things that I don't really mean to say. Sometimes I am a little too colorful. I make jokes and people don't laugh, they gasp. Other times, I delve into personal issues that I really don't mean to discuss. I tell stories that reveal personal things that are embarrassing to my spouse. Sometimes my stories seem to have a life of their own and ramble on for too long. I'm so eager to tell my story that I miss what other people are saying. I interrupt constantly and am uncomfortable if I'm not talking. I feel like I really don't belong. I get nervous before I go to parties, talk too much when I get there, drink more than I'd planned, and spend the ride home lamenting all my social gaffes. I'm at a lost to explain why I feel so different. Everyone else seems so at ease and comfortable. Where was I when everyone else was learning how to make small talk and to get

> **Poor self-control impacts almost all aspects of adjustment including work, family and social domains.**

along so well? I feel like I am on an emotional roller coaster. I go from being anxious, to being hyper-verbal, to being depressed after I'm around people. Sometimes it's easier to make up an excuse and just stay home. When things go wrong in my relationships, I get so frustrated and angry that I can't think straight. I get really worked up over little things that don't mean much. In the middle of arguments, I say things I regret. I don't know when to back down. I try to win every argument. It seems like I must have the last word. I think my spouse and kids don't like to be around me because I cause so much chaos. I'm so controlling and unrelenting that I am no fun to be around. I can't seem to calm down even when I am trying to walk away. Even when I know I should stop, I can't control my angry outbursts.

For many individuals with Attention-Deficit Hyperactivity Disorder (AD/HD), problems in peer relations that start in childhood persist into adolescence and adulthood (Murphy, 1998; Weiss and Hechtman, 1993). Adolescents with AD/HD tend to have fewer close relationships and have increased rates of peer rejection than teens without AD/HD (Bagwell, Molina, Pelham, and Hoza, 2001). Impaired social relations persist even when AD/HD symptoms diminish in adolescence, possibly due to a long history of tenuous peer relationships. Furthermore, as a result of "impulsivity, interrupting, forgetfulness, inattentiveness, hyperactivity, difficulty reading social cues, temper or mood swings, adults with AD/HD frequently report difficulties maintaining friendships" (Murphy, 1998, p. 583). Adults with AD/HD have been described as self-absorbed, impulsive, intrusive, inattentive, irresponsible, rude and insensitive in social situations (Murphy, 1998). Poor self-esteem and low self-confidence are common, and are often associated with isolation and feelings of loneliness. Thus, impaired social relationships appear to be a life-long problem for individuals with AD/HD. Many adults feel like they missed important lessons in life—how to express themselves, how to feel at ease, and how to control their emotions in social interactions. They have!

Current conceptualizations of AD/HD suggest that primary deficits in executive functions interfere with development of self-control (Barkley, 1997; Goldstein and Ellison, in press; Teeter, 1998). Poor self-control impacts almost all aspects of adjustment including work, family and social domains. Strayhorn (2002a) defined self-control as the ability to engage in "behaviors that result in delayed (but more) reward," and "doing something less immediately pleasurable than an alternative, because it has greater total expected benefit or is more ethical" (p. 7). Barkley (1997) describes self-control as "the ability to alter a behavior (or response), which in turn alters the consequence of that event" (p. 51). For individuals with AD/HD, poor self-control appears to be a major problem across the life span that has significant consequences on social functioning (Teeter, 1998).

Deficits in self-control make it difficult to (1) regulate one's emotions, (2) attend to verbal and non-verbal cues in social situations, and (3) control exaggerated temperament or over-reactivity to social situations. Emotional regulation involves the ability to counterbalance or change a strong reaction in the face of an external situation or event (Barkley, 1997). Temperamental over-reactivity, emotional outbursts and difficulties calming down may be problematic and make it difficult for adults to compromise and negotiate when conflicts arise. Frustration tolerance may also be poor,

so little things may get blown out of proportion. Problems with self-control make it difficult to engage in meaningful, intimate relationships that are built on reciprocal, caring interactions. Adults (and children) with AD/HD miss important verbal and non-verbal cues that may alert them to regulate their emotional reactions and to modify their behaviors when things are not going well in social interchanges. Oftentimes they are oblivious to the subtle cues that suggest we need to modify how we feel and behave.

The Consequences of Poor Self-Control

There are a number of other risk factors for poor adult adjustment that appear in part to be a consequence of poor self-control. These risk factors significantly interfere with normal adjustment, and may have severe consequences for the well-being of the individual:

♦ Sexual adjustment problems (e.g., earlier sexual experimentation, more sexual partners and increased risk for sexually transmitted diseases in adolescence)
♦ Higher rates of divorce and less marital satisfaction
♦ Comorbid alcohol, drug use/abuse
♦ Comorbid psychiatric problems (e.g., depression, anxiety)
♦ Comorbid personality disorders (e.g., anti-social, dependent)
♦ Frequent job changes and fewer advancements
♦ Reduced educational attainment

Considerations for Treating Adults with AD/HD

Unfortunately, there is little empirical evidence available on psychosocial treatments and few controlled studies on adults with AD/HD (Murphy, 1998). The following ideas are offered as promising clinical practices, and should be carefully monitored to determine progress and efficacy for the adult you may be working with. Some of these approaches are being successfully used in multimodal treatment plans at the University of Massachusetts Medical Center Adult AD/HD Clinic. Research is needed to determine the efficacy of these treatment options. See Strayhorn (2002b) for other promising strategies for increasing self-control in children.

Individual counseling or therapy might help adults develop better adjustment and interaction skills. The adult can practice self-control techniques through role playing with the therapist. Strategies for negotiating and compromising might be useful. Family or couples therapy may also be needed if relationships are dysfunctional or severely strained (Kilcarr, 2002).

Specific training in anger management might be useful when emotions are out of control or when constant arguments at home or at work interfere with adjustment. Anger management techniques might include: becoming aware of events that trigger anger, using calming statements and relaxation to prepare for stressors, and re-framing and re-structuring expectations (more realistic). Practice techniques with the therapist, then try them at work or at home. Keep an anger log to understand feelings and become aware of situations that go well. Re-think the plan when things don't go well. Plan alternative coping strategies (e.g., take a walk, break for 3–5 minutes before continuing conversation).

Practice self-control through setting achievable goals (e.g., improving relationships at work). Personal coaches may facilitate this process by structuring, monitoring and providing feedback when setting goals and trying new social skills (e.g., listening, regulating amount of talking, controlling emotional

> Medication may protect some teens with AD/HD from engaging in substance abuse.

tone of conversations). The adult is encouraged to take responsibility and to become more self-aware through on-going contact with the coach (Murphy, 1998). Short, directive and pragmatic approaches help identify strategies to meet goals, reinforcement for staying with a plan, and support and encouragement when things go wrong (Ratey, 2002). Although there is no empirical evidence showing that coaching is effective, it remains a commonly used intervention for adults (Murphy, 1998, 2002).

Seek treatment for other comorbid psychiatric problems (e.g., anxiety, depression, antisocial personality disorders) **and comorbid alcohol, drug use/abuse problems.** These problems will exacerbate social relationship difficulties and are typically not addressed in individual, family or anger management approaches.

Pharmacotherapy might also be considered as part of a multimodal plan for adults with AD/HD. Wilens and Prince (2002) review evidence that adults with AD/HD respond positively to stimulant medications. It is unclear whether medication will help to reduce social problems in adults, but there is promising research to suggest that medication can be "protective" for some adolescents with AD/HD. Although medication did not produce fewer peer problems, medicated teens appeared to have friends who engaged in more socially acceptable behaviors and less substance use (Bagwell et al., 2001). Further, medication may protect some teens with AD/HD from engaging in substance abuse (Biederman et al., 1999).

Bagwell et al. (2001) suggests that increased self-control that results from medication may reduce the number of rule violations and association with deviant peer groups. Other factors, such as parental supervision, may also affect this relationship. Although medication may have some protective actions, combined psychosocial and pharmacological treatments are most likely necessary for children and youth (MTA Cooperative Group, 1999). We need to apply the same rigorous multi-site, multi-method research methodology to determine effective treatment approaches for adults with AD/HD.

References

Bagwell, C. L., Molina, B. S., Pelham, W. E., & Hoza, B. (2001). Attention-deficit hyperactivity disorder and problems in peer relations: predictions from childhood to adolescence. *Journal of the American Academy of Child and Adolescent Psychiatry, 40,* 1285–1292.

Barkley, R. (1997). *AD/HD and the nature of self-control.* New York: Guilford Press.

Biederman, J., Wilens, T., Mick, E., Spencer, T., & Faraone, S. (1999). Pharmacotherapy of attention-deficit hyperactivity disorder reduces risk for substance use disorder. *Pediatrics, 104,* 20.

Goldstein, S., & Ellison, P.A. Teeter (eds). (2002). *Clinician's guide to adult ADHD: Assessment and intervention.* San Diego, CA: Academic Press.

Kilcarr, P. (2002). Making marriages work for individuals with AD/HD. In S. Goldstein & A. Teeter Ellison (eds). *Clinician's guide to adult ADHD: Assessment and intervention.* San Diego, CA: Academic Press.

MTA Cooperative Group, (1999). A 14-month randomized trial of treatment strategies for attention-deficit hyperactivity disorder. *Archives of General Psychiatry, 56,* 1073–1086.

Murphy, K. (1998). Psychological counseling in adults with AD/HD. In R. Barkley (Ed.), *Attention-deficit hyperactivity disorder: A hand book for diagnosis and treatment* (pp. 582–591). New York: Guilford Press.

Murphy, K. (2002). Clinical case studies. In S. Goldstein & A. Teeter Ellison (eds). *Clinician's guide to adult ADHD: Assessment and intervention.* San Diego, CA: Academic Press.

Ratey, N. (2002). Life coaching for adult AD/HD. In S. Goldstein & A. Teeter Ellison (eds). *Clinician's guide to adult ADHD: Assessment and intervention.* San Diego, CA: Academic Press.

Strayhorn, J. M. (2002a). Self-control: Theory and research. *Journal of the American Academy of Child and Adolescent Psychiatry, 41,* 7–16.

Strayhorn, J. M. (2002b). Self-control: Toward systematic training programs. *Journal of the American Academy of Child and Adolescent Psychiatry, 41,* 17–27.

Teeter, P. A. (1998). *Interventions for AD/HD: Treatment in developmental context.* New York: Guilford Press.

Weiss, G., & Hechtman, L. (1993). *Hyperactive children grown up (2nd ed): AD/HD in children, adolescents and adults.* New York: Guilford Press.

Wilens, T., & Prince, J. (2002). Pharmacotherapy of adult ADHD. In S. Goldstein & A. Teeter Ellison (eds). *Clinician's guide to adult ADHD: Assessment and intervention.* San Diego, CA: Academic Press.

Phyllis Anne Teeter Ellison, Ed.D., is president of CHADD (2005–07) and a member of the Editorial Advisory Board. Sam Goldstein, Ph.D., is a member of CHADD's Professional Advisory Board (2005–08), a member of the Editorial Advisory Board, and former chair of the Professional Advisory Board. He is a member of the faculty at the University of Utah.

This article first appeared in *Attention!*® magazine, April 2002.

Dealing with the Impact of AD/HD on Marriage

By Michael T. Bell, N.C.C., L.P.C.

While any marriage has its challenging moments, when one or both spouses have AD/HD, those times only seem to multiply. Noted psychologist Arthur L. Robin, Ph.D., recently discussed the characteristics of AD/HD marriages throughout the course of a relationship (October 2002 *Attention!*®). He explained that during the courtship phase of the relationship, the positive aspects of AD/HD often dominate. However, as the relationship progresses, responsibilities build and the newness of the relationship wears off, the less endearing aspects of AD/HD can frequently negatively impact a relationship. He also cited eight behaviors that are often problematic to relationships where one of the individuals has AD/HD. These eight behaviors are:

1. Doesn't remember being told to do things.
2. Saying things without thinking.
3. "Zoning out" in conversations.
4. Problems dealing with frustrations.
5. Trouble getting started on a task.
6. Under-estimating time needed to complete a task.
7. Leaving a mess.
8. Not finishing household projects.

This article will take the information presented in Dr. Robin's article a step further by discussing some of the interventions that can be helpful in reducing the negative impact of these eight behaviors.

Doesn't Remember Being Told to Do Things

Intervention 1

Make proper use of memory prompts and make the regular and consistent use of prompts a habit for life even when it seems boring, inconvenient or frustrating to do so. Memory prompts can include:

♦ Leaving messages on your home or work answering machines to remind you of things you need to do when you arrive at home or at the office.
♦ Using stickers and sticky notes.
♦ Using alarms.
♦ Creating "To Do" lists.
♦ Sending yourself e-mails.
♦ Putting things you need to remember by the front door.
♦ Creating your own memory cues, things that have worked in the past, such as checking your "To Do List" at the end of every day.

You are using memory prompts properly when you set the prompts up immediately and don't have to remember to set them up later.

Intervention 2

Be aware of the rationalizations that keep you from properly using memory prompts. Don't let your internal rationalization statements like, "I'll write it down in a minute," sabotage your use of memory prompts. Be aware of these statements and how they sabotage your success so that you can avoid giving into them.

Intervention 3

Realize that you are not going to remember what you were told to do if you never stop to listen in the first place. Reduce all other distractions, stop thinking about other things, and intentionally focus on what the other person is saying. If necessary, repeat back to him or her what you heard. Go ahead and write down what you need to remember on your "To Do" list or set up some other prompt right away.

Saying Things without Thinking

Intervention 1

Be aware of your verbal impulsiveness in public settings and the topics that make your spouse or significant other uncomfortable. Be considerate when it comes to discussing personal topics with others.

Intervention 2

Learn how to engage others in conversation. Encourage them to talk about themselves and their interests. You might not say a single thing about yourself and the other person will leave the conversation thinking that you are a fascinating individual. And while it might be a good idea to avoid certain topics (e.g., sex, religion, politics), it is normally safe to find out about kids, hobbies, areas of interest and jobs.

Intervention 3

Try to be aware of how others are reacting to you when you are speaking. If they appear uncomfortable or are trying to change the topic, recognize that. It is also important to realize that adults with AD/HD often enjoy intense conversations because it feeds their need for stimulation. Most other individuals do not have this same need, or at least not to the same extent. Conversations that you find fun or exciting might make others feel uncomfortable.

Intervention 4

Help your spouse understand AD/HD better so that he or she will be less defensive and not personalize things when you *do* say something without thinking.

Intervention 5

When your spouse's feelings are hurt by something that you said impulsively, don't negate his or her feelings. Be patient, listen to why what you said was hurtful, and try not to become defensive so you can really hear his or her concerns.

> **AD/HD behaviors with the greatest negative impact on relationships**
>
> - Doesn't remember being told things
> - Says things without thinking
> - "Zones out" in conversations
> - Has trouble dealing with frustration
> - Has trouble getting started on a task
> - Under-estimates time needed to complete a task
> - Leaves a mess
> - Doesn't finish household projects

"Zoning Out" During Conversations

Intervention 1

Realize what listening really communicates to your spouse. It tells him or her that:
- You value his or her opinion.
- You think what he or she has to say is important.
- You care about him or her.

Intervention 2

Practice the following listening steps:

Step One: Limit or eliminate all other distractions. For example, mute the TV, turn off the radio or turn away from the computer.

Step Two: Take a deep breath, slowly inhale and exhale. Quiet your mind and relax. As you breathe out, feel the tension leave your body. If there is anything you are focusing your mind on, make a quick note of it to yourself, then let go of it and focus your full attention on your spouse. Use a relaxed gaze (what some people refer to as soft eyes). This will help you relieve tension while you are listening.

Step Three: While your spouse is speaking, listen carefully. Do not:

♦ Think about what you were just doing.

♦ Think about what you are going to do when your spouse finishes talking.

♦ Think about what you are going to say in response to your spouse.

♦ Think about topics unrelated to this conversation.

Simply open your mind to take in what your spouse is saying. If you find your mind wandering to other things, recognize this and refocus your attention.

> People with AD/HD often avoid activities that require an extended period of concentration and focus.

Intervention 3

As an adult with AD/HD, it can be very difficult to stay focused and listen to what your spouse or significant other is saying. If it is not a good time to listen to your spouse, calmly let your spouse know that you will listen to him or her when you have completed your task. However, your current task should be worthy of postponing your spouse, and not a reason to continue watching TV, surfing the Internet or the like.

Trouble Dealing with Frustrations

Intervention 1

Actively work on reducing the areas of frustration in your life, which may help you feel less overwhelmed and irritated.

For many individuals with AD/HD, the number one cause of frustration can be their tendency to lose or misplace things. A principle that can help to combat this is, *"everything has a place, its place is the same place all the time, and I am responsible for putting it in its place as* soon as I am done with it." This is a no excuses kind of rule. As soon as we make excuses for not putting things where they belong, they get lost and our frustrations build.

Intervention 2

When it is feasible to do so, hire someone to handle some of the things that you find frustrating. For instance, if house cleaning is frustrating, hire a housekeeper. If household projects like building a deck are frustrating, then hire a carpenter.

Trouble Getting Started on a Task

People with AD/HD often avoid activities that require an extended period of concentration and focus. The problem is that one still needs to take care of things that are not stimulating and/or require an extended period of concentration and focus. They still need to be done and the best way to deal with them is in a proactive manner.

Intervention 1

The goal here is to *"figure out what it is you are avoiding the most and take care of it first."* In short, to gain proper control over the impact of your AD/HD, you must learn to *avoid avoidance*.

Intervention 2

Learn how to train yourself to first take care of things you might intentionally want to avoid and don't allow yourself to get away with those old behaviors. Consider small rewards for yourself for accomplishing tedious but necessary tasks.

Under-Estimating the Time Needed to Complete a Task

Intervention 1

Determine the average amount of time you under-estimate how long it will take you to finish a task and as a general rule of thumb, purposefully add that time onto any estimate. For instance, if it normally takes twice as long to complete a task as you think it is going to take, then make it a habit to double the amount of time you give yourself.

Intervention 2

Ask someone who has done the task previously how long it took them. Take that time and add an extra time allowance to complete that task within a reasonable period.

Intervention 3

It is important to learn the concept of under-promising and over-delivering. If you get the task done earlier than you said you would, your spouse will be happy. If it takes longer than you stated, then they will be dissatisfied. Given this point, it is best to under-promise and over-deliver.

Leaving a Mess and Not Finishing Household Projects

Intervention 1

Take a second look at the idea of *avoiding avoidance*. Both problematic behaviors listed above are often caused because avoidance has occurred. That project, which was interesting at first, has lost its intrinsic interest or excitement and so you avoid completing it. That stack of papers does not get picked up because you think you will take care of it later. In the end, the stack of papers does not get picked up or that project does not get finished. This is because neither task is stimulating and both cause frustration because their completion is no longer rewarding to you. However, the reality is that life will be better for you and your spouse if you go ahead and complete them.

Intervention 2

Realize that your spouse's need for neatness, order and completion is just as valid as your need for stimulation. Be willing to put forth the effort to meet his or her needs. All these interventions can be helpful in sustaining a happy and successful marriage, but seeking the assistance of a marriage counselor who is cognizant of the impact of AD/HD on relationships may also help your relationship. It is important to understand that AD/HD alone may not be to blame for all of the issues that arise in our marriages. A good marriage counselor should be able to help you determine which issues are affected by AD/HD and which are not.

Michael T. Bell, N.C.C., L.P.C. is a psychotherapist in private practice in Manassas, Va., and the author of *You, Your Relationship & Your ADD: A Workbook.*

This article first appeared in *Attention!*® magazine, April 2003.

Diagnosing and Treating Women with AD/HD

By Kathleen G. Nadeau, Ph.D

AD/HD is one of the most highly researched childhood psychiatric conditions; however, less than one percent of that research has focused on the issues of girls, and even less research has addressed women with AD/HD. We do not yet have good statistics about the numbers of girls or women with AD/HD, but current evidence suggests that girls have been seriously under-diagnosed. Joseph Biederman, M.D., the leader of a major AD/HD research group at Massachusetts General Hospital in Boston, considers the under-diagnosis of females to be a serious public health concern.

Diagnosis

A major barrier in the diagnosis of women with AD/HD is that the current diagnostic criteria were developed to describe young

boys with hyperactive/impulsive patterns. Gender-appropriate diagnostic criteria are badly needed. A self-report questionnaire for women with AD/HD, the Self-assessment Symptom Inventory (SASI) has recently been developed to help address this problem. However, research to validate the SASI and to develop norms remains to be done. Self-report questionnaires for both women and girls can be found at www.addvance.com. (At present, these questionnaires should be used as structured interviews, and cannot be considered diagnostic tools.)

Few mental health professionals in practice today have received training in the diagnosis of adults with AD/HD, and even fewer in the diagnosis of women. As a result, when a woman seeks diagnosis and treatment, she faces a difficult challenge to find a professional who is aware of the different ways that AD/HD may present in females. Women may struggle with significant AD/HD issues, but remain undiagnosed because they don't meet the current diagnostic criteria. Several common barriers to diagnosis are:

The requirement that age of onset is prior to age seven.
The majority of females fall into the "predominantly inattentive" type of AD/HD. Recent studies have confirmed what many clinicians have observed—that many of those with primarily inattentive AD/HD do not

manifest symptoms that are noted in early childhood. In addition, there is some evidence that many girls do not manifest symptoms until puberty, when fluctuating female hormones intensify AD/HD symptoms.

The requirement that impairment in two or more settings be documented in childhood. Academic impairment in the classroom—the pattern that most clinicians look for—may not be evident in the elementary school years. Girls tend to work harder for teacher approval, and work harder to hide their attentional difficulties. Girls with mediocre academic performance may be dismissed as "average" with no consideration of possible AD/HD. Furthermore, girls are much less likely to be oppositional, defiant, or have behavior problems in the classroom that would result in referral for treatment.

Females are less likely to be hyperactive/impulsive, and the behavior of those who are, may look very different than males. Most teachers are trained to look for hyperactivity and impulsivity in children with AD/HD. Most girls with AD/HD don't show signs of hyperactivity. And the patterns of hyperactivity in girls may look very different than those of boys. They may be hyper-talkative, hyper-social, or hyper-reactive emotionally.

Mental health professionals are more familiar with conditions that commonly co-exist with AD/HD and are prone to focus on these while overlooking AD/HD.
Females with AD/HD are more likely to struggle with co-existing anxiety and depression. Clinicians familiar with these diagnoses are more likely to recognize and treat the anxiety and depression, while overlooking the co-existing and possibly primary AD/HD.

Protective factors may delay the onset of AD/HD symptoms.
Girls with AD/HD who do not have co-existing conditions such as learning disabilities, who

have a high IQ, and who have supportive family and school environments may not manifest AD/HD symptoms until much later. Women with a history of average or above average academic achievement during school years may find that their AD/HD concerns are dismissed because they don't fit the expected patterns.

> All too often, women seek diagnosis for AD/HD only to be told their childhood history is 'inconsistent' with an AD/HD diagnosis.

   All too often, women seek diagnosis for AD/HD only to be told their childhood history is "inconsistent" with an AD/HD diagnosis. Most often, such women are diagnosed and treated for a co-existing condition such as anxiety or depression, while their AD/HD is ignored.

Treatment
Many women with AD/HD never receive an appropriate diagnosis. Women who are diagnosed with AD/HD face the challenge of receiving appropriate treatment.

Physician reluctance to prescribe stimulants to adult women.
Some clinicians are inexperienced in treating adults with AD/HD and are uncomfortable prescribing stimulant medication to adults. Although stimulants have been well established as the first-line medication for treating AD/HD, many physicians opt for a second-line treatment such as an antidepressant, which may be less effective.

Hormonal issues in medical treatment.
Recent research has explored the important role that estrogen plays in the cognitive functioning of women. It is well known that some women experience significant problems with moodiness and depression during low estrogen states such

> While many men with AD/HD build support systems around them, women are expected to be the support system for others.

as the premenstrual period each month, the postpartum period following birth, in peri-menopause and menopause. We're now beginning to recognize that low estrogen states also have a strong impact on cognitive functioning that can increase AD/HD symptoms in females.

When an adult with AD/HD reports that stimulant medication has become less effective, the most common physician response is to increase the stimulant dose. This approach may not be appropriate or effective, however, if the problem has resulted from declining estrogen. Very few physicians recognize this estrogen connection and take it into consideration in planning treatment.

Co-existing Conditions

Appropriate, effective treatment becomes even more challenging when co-existing conditions complicate the diagnostic and treatment picture. Often, in those cases in which a woman has received prior treatment for a co-existing condition, her AD/HD has never been identified and treated. Studies show that treatment success is much greater when the AD/HD is diagnosed and appropriately treated along with co-existing conditions.

Typically, because the recognition of AD/HD in women is still very recent, clinicians are not experienced in combination treatments for AD/HD and co-existing conditions. Clinicians may mistake hyperactive/impulsive behavior patterns in women for bipolar symptoms. In women who have both bipolar disorder and AD/HD, clinicians may fear that stimulant medication for AD/HD may trigger a manic episode, and are reluctant to prescribe stimulants. Others may not be aware that stimu-

lants may not be tolerated and effective in women with significant anxiety, unless the anxiety is well controlled with medication.

Common co-existing conditions in women include:
♦ Depression
♦ Sleep disorders
♦ Anxiety
♦ Eating disorders
♦ Bipolar disorder
♦ Addictions

Psychological Treatment

Aside from medication treatment issues, women with AD/HD face different challenges that need to be addressed in therapies specifically designed for them.

The challenges of motherhood

Most parenting programs, including those for children with AD/HD, begin with an assumption that the mother does *not* have AD/HD and will be able to implement and maintain systems for her child with AD/HD. New parenting programs need to be developed that help the mother and child take charge of AD/HD issues in the home.

Self-esteem issues

Recent research suggests that women, more than men, struggle with low self-esteem as a result of their AD/HD. Therapy designed for women needs to directly address this issue—helping women to reframe their view of AD/HD, helping them to stop blaming and criticizing themselves, and helping them to develop a more positive self-image.

Social skills and interpersonal relationships

Research suggests that even as early as pre-school, females with AD/HD experience social rejection or social neglect that impacts them very negatively, contributing to their low self-esteem. Treatment programs for females—girls as well as women—should focus on their need to address their social skill deficits, as well as actively create a more accepting social environment in their work and personal lives.

The challenges of daily life

While many men with AD/HD build support systems around them—administrative assistants, business partners, wives—who can assist them in daily life tasks and organization, women traditionally are expected to *be* the support system for others. At work, they are less likely to be in a position to have an administrative assistant, and more likely to be in a job that requires *them* to perform administrative tasks. At home, most women still play the role of primary parent and homemaker.

Treatment of women needs to focus on:

♦ Becoming more realistic in their expectations of themselves
♦ Creating more AD/HD-friendly home environments
♦ Developing and maintaining organizational strategies
♦ Utilizing time-management techniques to meet multiple daily demands
♦ Giving themselves permission to seek the support they need

Where Do We Go from Here?

We are at the beginning of a very exciting journey. Growing recognition of the unique issues of girls and women by CHADD and other advocacy organizations is an important first step in gaining the knowledge that we need to accurately identify and appropriately treat women with AD/HD.

AD/HD research needs to focus more on the needs of girls and women—developing more appropriate diagnostic criteria and exploring treatment approaches that may be more effective for females.

Clinician training is desperately needed on gender issues related to AD/HD. Few clinicians are familiar with the unique issues of women.

For now, women must serve as their own best advocates, working to develop awareness, and working to educate the professionals in their community about the diagnostic and treatment issues of women with AD/HD.

Kathleen G. Nadeau, Ph.D., is co-editor, with Patricia Quinn, M.D., of two recently published books on women's AD/HD issues, *Understanding Women with AD/HD,* and *Gender Issues and AD/HD.* Dr. Nadeau is also the co-author of *Understanding Girls with AD/HD* a book on the AD/HD issues of girls. She also co-founded the National Center for Gender Issues and AD/HD (NCGI), a non-profit advocacy organization for girls and women with AD/HD (www.ncgiadd.org). Dr. Nadeau has served on CHADD's Professional Advisory Board.

This article first appeared in *Attention!*® magazine, October 2002.

AD/HD and Organization: A Collision Course?

By Judith Kolberg

Life requires us to be on time, have a plan, prioritize and re-prioritize, *and* get rid of clutter—the activities we call being organized. But many adults with AD/HD are on a collision course with organization. That's because most AD/HD patterns run counter to the "patterns" it takes to be organized.

Distractibility

Organizing requires attentiveness, a kind of single-minded focus over at least a brief period of time in order to get the job done. But distractibility, one of AD/HD's hallmark traits, couldn't be more at odds with this requirement. Take de-cluttering your dining room table, for example. You finally hear it scream, "Organize me! Get this month's worth of mail off of me!" So you begin opening the mail with great gusto. But the credit card offer you just opened is too hard to ignore. You start looking for your current APR so you can compare it to the new offer. Now you are deep inside your financial files and you take the opportunity to toss out a few ancient bank statements. The trip to the trash takes you into the kitchen where the counter needs a good cleaning, so you go under the sink in search of a clean sponge. There you see that the cleaning products need to be organized. It turns out to be a big, dirty

> Many adults with AD/HD are on a collision course with organization.

job that simply must end with a quick shower. On your way to the bathroom, you pass the dining room table, remembering that your original goal was to clear the clutter.

So what can you do? First, give yourself a break. Then, take responsibility for your disorganization by learning how to cope given your AD/HD. Here's how:

Strengthen your intentions, weaken your distractions

- ♦ Set an alarm for 15 minutes. De-clutter the dining room table for all of that time. Don't go anywhere or do anything else. At the end of 15 minutes, run your errands to the trash or the filing cabinet. Then come back for another 15-minute round.
- ♦ Take "green" breaks. If you feel fidgety, work for 10 minutes and break for five minutes. A green break is just that. Go outdoors. Look at something green. It is calming and restoring to the brain. Stretch, breathe and bend, but don't go far afield. Drink water and come on back.
- ♦ Self-talk yourself back to the task at hand. Say out loud, "What do I need to be doing right now?" or "Where was I before I got distracted?" It's important that you self-talk out loud so you can overcome any internal distractions.
- ♦ Reward yourself in proportion to the organizing chore. A de-cluttered dining room table deserves at least a massage or a new CD.

Cut clutter off at the source

♦ Use less plastic (credit cards)—it just means more paper. Get yourself down to one solid, low-interest credit card.

♦ Limit your subscriptions to magazines and news-letters. Do you really need *Time* magazine **and** *Newsweek*?

♦ Dump the catalogs unless you are ready to order the same week they arrive. I promise you'll get another catalog in six weeks.

And, most importantly,

♦ Develop the routine of opening your mail every day.

Stimulation

A stimulation-seeking brain is another AD/HD trait that runs counter to organizing. Organizing is notoriously bor-ing. That's because organizing is a means to an end, not an end in itself. It's sup-posed to be a little dull so you can reap its benefits without being absorbed by its utility. Take filing for example. It is not exactly stimu-lating to pick up a piece of paper, create a file and stick it in a filing cabinet. But let the filing mount up, causing a few frantic searches or the havoc of hiding stacks of papers when compa-ny comes, and now we're talking stimulating!

We call this the "critical mass" approach to organizing. Sometimes, just waiting until the stacks are about to fall over or the late fees are mounting up provides the critical mass to motivate organizing. But the price you pay in stress for losing important papers or the feeling of being overwhelmed all the time, plus the ugliness of stacks of papers everywhere, is not worth it.

Organize every day

♦ File documents, read newsletters, process the daily mail, pay bills and put things away every day. All in all, it will take you about an hour, but will pay off in reduced stress, faster retrieval and a feeling of control.

Spice things up a little

♦ File with music on
♦ Organize with a friend
♦ Use beautiful containers and colorful file folders

Out of Sight, Out of Mind

Many adults with AD/HD are OosOoms (out-of-sight-out-of-mind). You need to keep things out in full view in order to remember to deal with them. For instance,

> From an organizing point of view, hyperfocusing can wreak havoc on planning.

if your weed-trimmer needs re-wiring, you might leave it on a living room chair with pictures to be framed. Have to return library books or videos? Not a chance—unless you trip over them on the way out the door. It makes perfect sense to keep things in sight and in mind if you are an adult with AD/HD, but from an organizing point of view, a negative cycle begins. You keep things in view, they mount up, you get anxious, and pretty soon the compelling reason for taking action gets lost.

Use your creativity to keep items visible
- ♦ Keep things in sight, but attractively. Use see-through folders, nice baskets and terrific looking clear containers.
- ♦ Retire your filing cabinet. Go for crates-on-casters. They're open, easy to see inside, and easy to stash inside a closet when company comes.
- ♦ Use multiple reminders like sticky note messages on the bathroom mirror, on the dashboard of the car, and stuck to your day planner.

Hyperfocus

When really engaged, nobody can beat an adult with AD/HD for concentration. But from an organizing point of view, hyperfocusing can wreak havoc on planning. How many times have you planned time with your family, then picked up your e-mail, journeyed out on the Web, and returned from your virtual trip only to be late for that reality-based recital, picnic or ballgame?

- ♦ Know your hyperfocus traps and avoid them when other commitments need attention. Common traps are: Web surfing, on-line investing, computer games, reading the newspaper, browsing catalogues, watching TV and shopping.
- ♦ Snap yourself out of hyperfocus by setting a loud alarm, computer reminder or arranging for someone to interrupt you.

Organizing can be difficult for even the most well organized among us, but it is especially challenging for adults with AD/HD. Appreciate that fact about your life and go on from there. It is very easy to adopt someone else's expectations for being organized as your own. There is a lot of pressure out there to "get it right." Get it right, for you and your needs.

Judith Kolberg is the co-author of the 2002 book, *ADD-Friendly Ways to Organize Your Life,* with Dr. Kathleen Nadeau. Her book, *Conquering Chronic Disorganization* is available from Amazon.com. Kolberg is a professional organizer and founder of the National Study Group on Chronic Disorganization.

This article first appeared in *Attention!*® magazine, October 2002.

Succeeding in the Workplace

The symptoms of AD/HD create special challenges for the adult in the workplace, just as they do for the child in school. To date, very little research has been conducted that provides adults with AD/HD empirically-based approaches to understanding and coping with workplace issues. Until scientifically-based guidelines are available, it may prove useful to follow the procedures commonly used by career counselors to guide individuals in selecting a job and coping with AD/HD on the job. This article will:

- offer tips for improving on-the-job functioning
- describe the rights of individuals under the Americans with Disabilities Act and the Rehabilitation Act of 1973
- provide guidelines for making career choices

The assistance of a career counselor or a psychologist, social worker, or other health care worker with career counseling training is extremely helpful in understanding and maximizing these factors. Some individuals, however, may be able to carry out the steps discussed in this sheet with the help of questionnaires, checklists, and suggestions given in the career counseling books on the reference list.

Improving On-the-Job Functioning

Some adults with AD/HD have very successful careers. Others may struggle with a variety of challenges, including poor communication skills, distractibility, procrastination, and difficulty managing complex projects. Each individual with AD/HD has a different set of challenges. Therefore, it is important to consider your unique picture, as you go about designing strategies, accommodations and modifications for the workplace. Below are suggestions for coping with many of the symptoms or impairments associated with AD/HD.

1. Distractibility

Problems with external distractibility (noises and movement in the surrounding environment) and internal distractibility (daydreams) can be the biggest challenge for adults with AD/HD. The following strategies may help:

- Request a private office or quiet cubicle, or take work home or work when others are not in the office.
- Use "white noise" earphones, classical music or other sounds to drown out office noises.
- Work in unused space, such as a conference room, where distractions are few.
- Route phone calls directly to voicemail, and respond to them at a set time every day.
- Jot down ideas in a notebook to avoid interruption of the current task.
- Keep a list of ideas that come to you during meetings so that you can communicate more effectively.
- Perform one task at a time. Do not start a new task until the current one is done.

2. Impulsivity

Adults with AD/HD may struggle with impulsivity and temper outbursts in the workplace. Try the following strategies:

- Learn to use self-talk to monitor impulsive actions.
- Work with a coach to role-play appropriate responses to frustrating situations.
- Ask for regular, constructive feedback as a way of becoming more aware of how impulsivity might manifest in you.

♦ Practice relaxation and meditation techniques.

♦ Anticipate the problems that regularly trigger impulsive reactions and develop routines for coping with these situations.

3. Hyperactivity

Adults with the hyperactive type of AD/HD often do better in jobs that allow a great deal of movement, such as sales, but if you have a sedentary job, the following strategies may help:

> Adults with the hyperactive type of AD/HD often do better in jobs that allow a great deal of movement, such as sales.

♦ Take intermittent breaks to do photo-copying, go to the mailroom, or walk to the water fountain.

♦ Take notes in meetings to prevent restlessness.

♦ Move around, exercise, take a walk, or run up and down the stairs.

♦ Bring lunch—instead of going out to buy it—so the lunch hour can be a time for exercise.

4. Poor Memory

Failing to remember deadlines and other responsibilities can antagonize coworkers, especially when working on a team. To improve memory, try the suggestions below:

♦ Use tape recording devices or take copious notes at meetings.

♦ Write checklists for complicated tasks.

♦ Use a bulletin board or computer reminder list for announcements and other memory triggers.

♦ Learn how to use a day planner and keep it with you to keep track of tasks and events.

♦ Write notes on sticky pads and put them in a highly visible place.

5. Boredom-blockouts

Because of their strong need for stimulation, some adults with AD/HD become easily bored at work, especially with detailed paperwork and routine tasks. To prevent boredom, try the following tips:

♦ Set a timer to stay on task.

♦ Break up long tasks into shorter ones.

♦ Take breaks, drink water, get up and walk around.

♦ Find a job with stimulating responsibilities and minimal routine tasks.

6. Time management difficulties

Managing time can be a big challenge for adults with AD/HD. Here are some guidelines for improving time management skills:

♦ Use time-line charts to break large projects into smaller pieces, with sub due-dates.

♦ Reward yourself for achieving sub due-dates.

♦ Use watch devices with alarms, buzzers, planners or computer planning software.

♦ Program your computer to beep 5 minutes before every meeting on the calendar.

♦ Avoid over-scheduling the day by overestimating how long each task or meeting will take.

See the What We Know sheet entitled, "Time Management: Learning to Use a Day Planner," at www.help4adhd.org/en/about.

7. Procrastination

Putting things off not only prevents completion of tasks, but also creates problems for others on the team. Here are some strategies for success:

♦ Break the task into small pieces, rewarding yourself along the way. (Rewards need not be grand; they might be a new CD, a long walk with your dog, dancing, or whatever you enjoy.) It may be helpful to have a coach or someone else to whom you can report and be accountable for achieving each piece of the task, until you learn to overcome your tendencies to procrastinate. See the What We Know sheet on coaching at www.help4adhd.org/en/about.

♦ Ask the supervisor to set a deadline for tasks.

♦ Consider working on a team with a co-worker who manages time well.

8. Difficulty managing long-term projects

Managing complex or long-term projects may be the hardest organizational challenge for adults with AD/HD. Managing projects requires a range of skills, including time management, organizing materials, tracking progress, and communicating accomplishments. Try the following guidelines:

♦ Break projects up into manageable parts, with rewards for completing each.

♦ Strive to shorten the time allowed on a project to better utilize "sprinting abilities."

♦ Ask a coach to assist you in tolerating longer and longer projects, a bit at a time.

♦ Find and partner with a co-worker who has good organizational skills.

♦ Look for work that requires only short-term tasks.

9. Paperwork/details

The inability to find important papers, turn in reports and timesheets, and maintain a filing system can create the impression of carelessness. If paperwork is a significant part of the job, try these tips:

♦ Make it a rule to handle each piece of paper only once.

♦ Ask an administrative assistant to handle detailed paperwork.

♦ Keep only those papers that are currently in use; purge the rest.

♦ Make filing more fun by color coding folders and using catchy labels.

I0. Interpersonal/social skill issues

Individuals with AD/HD may unintentionally offend co-workers by interrupting frequently, talking too much, being too blunt, or not listening well. If social skills are a challenge, try the following strategies:

> Managing complex or long-term projects may be the hardest organizational challenge for adults with AD/HD.

♦ Ask others for feedback, especially if there is a history of problems with colleagues and supervisors.

♦ Learn to pick up on social cues more readily. Some adults with AD/HD have a hard time picking up nonverbal cues that they are angering a co-worker or supervisor.

♦ Work with a coach to determine what types of settings often lead to interpersonal/social issues.

♦ Seek a position with greater autonomy if working with others is challenging.

See the What We Know sheet entitled, "Social Skills in Adults with AD/HD," for more information on improving social skills at www.help4adhd.org/en/about. Consult the books on the reference list for additional suggestions.

The Americans with Disabilities Act and the Rehabilitation Act of 1973

Two federal laws—The Rehabilitation Act of 1973 (RA) and the Americans with Disabilities Act of 1990 (ADA)—prohibit workplace discrimination against individuals with disabilities. The RA prohibits discrimination in three areas: (1) employment by the executive branch of the federal government, (2) employment by most federal government contractors, and (3) activities funded by federal subsidies or grants, including organizations receiving federal funding.

The ADA extends the concepts of the RA to (1) private employers with 15 or more employees, (2) all activities of state and local governments, including employment, and (3) "places of public accommodation," including most private schools and higher education institutions.

It is important to understand that being diagnosed with AD/HD does not automatically make an individual eligible for protection or accommodations under the RA or ADA. The protections of these laws extend to individuals who meet four conditions:

♦ They are individuals with disabilities under the law;
♦ They are otherwise qualified for the position, with or without reasonable accommodations;
♦ They are being excluded from employment solely by reasons of their disability; and

♦ They are covered by the applicable federal law.

To be eligible for the protection offered by the ADA and RA, an employee must disclose the disability to the employer. The decision to disclose a disability to an employer or not can be a difficult one. On the one hand, an employer is not required to make accommodations unless the employee has disclosed the disability. On the other hand, discrimination often begins when the employee makes the disclosure. These factors must be weighed before making the decision to disclose.

Reasons for not disclosing:
♦ If you do not need accommodations
♦ If you are performing well on the job
♦ If you feel that disclosing your disability will cause your supervisor and co-workers to discriminate against you

Reasons for disclosing:
♦ If you fear losing your job because you haven't received the accommodations you need to succeed
♦ If you are about to be fired because of performance issues

It is possible to request accommodations without disclosing information about the disability. First, if possible, try to provide the accommodations yourself—by coming in early or staying late to avoid distractions, for instance, or by programming the computer to remind you of appointments. Second, frame requests to the supervisor from a position of strength, rather than bringing up the disability. For example, instead of saying:

"I have a disability called AD/HD, which makes it hard for me to remember things and follow through,"

it might be better to reframe from a standpoint of strength, by saying,

"I work best when I use a tape recorder to help me remember everything new, until I get proficient."

Similarly, instead of:

"I know that the Americans with Disabilities Act protects those of us with disabilities from discrimination, so I know that you will need to provide me with special accommodations,"

it might be better to reframe from a standpoint of strength, by saying,

"I believe my strengths are consistent with the essential tasks of this job. If I can take the time to review my notes in a quiet place before each meeting, I can assure you that I can excel at this position."

Read the What We Know sheet entitled, "Legal Issues for Adults with AD/HD in the Workplace and Higher Education," at www.help4adhd.org/en/about for more information on ADA and RA.

Making a Career Change

Sometimes, no matter how hard they try, adults with AD/HD find that their initial career choice does not play to their strengths, and it is necessary to make a change. The following categories reflect aspects of an individual that impact effective functioning on the job. Collect data about each of these categories as it applies to you. This data will permit you to see yourself as a unique, complete person, and to better evaluate the careers that match your characteristics.

1. Interests (professional & leisure)
Since individuals with AD/HD work better in fields that interest them, it is important that they identify their interests. After the interests have been identified, a consultation with a trained career counselor, who can provide a list of occupations or jobs that correspond to their interests,

should be considered. The list of occupations that correspond to the individual's interests will provide the basis for the steps that follow.

2. Skills (mental, interpersonal and physical)
Identifying skills and accomplishments can reveal marketable skills that can be used in various work settings. Generally, skills fall into three categories: skills working with data, people or things. People do best when their skills correspond to the requirements of the job. Skills can be assessed through standardized tests or through checklists that trigger knowledge of success in past accomplishments.

For example, you might ask yourself the following questions:

♦ What subjects were easiest for you in school?
♦ What strengths do you think others see in you?
♦ What skills do you possess that enabled you to succeed in something?
♦ What strengths do you think teachers saw in you?
♦ What things about your job performance set you apart from others?

In addition, using a skill word list provided by a career counselor or published in a career book may be helpful in identifying skills that may not have been considered important or considered at all.

3. Personality
What type of personality are you? Personality preferences can be measured by standardized testing or by checklists that force you to choose between two situations. Knowing personality strengths can help improve work

> Sometimes adults with AD/HD find that their initial career choice does not play to their strengths, and it is necessary to make a change.

habits, increase career options, and achieve a more successful path to a career future.

4. Values (work and leisure)

People value different things. It is generally agreed that people work harder and with more focus when the task at hand is in line with their values. Leisure values are also important, because a personal passion can often turn into a career. Career counselors and other professionals who work with career issues, or checklists in career books, can help isolate these values.

5. Aptitudes (verbal, numerical, abstract reasoning, clerical speed and accuracy, mechanical, spatial, spelling, and language)

An aptitude is defined as the ability to acquire proficiency in a specific area. It often seems that these are innate, but this is not necessarily true. Aptitudes can also be learned. While a skill is a current ability, an aptitude is the potential to acquire a skill based upon natural talents or training.

Aptitudes can be formally assessed by a professional or by using informal checklists. When you understand what your strengths are, you can compare them to the requirements of any given job. *The Dictionary of Occupational Titles* and *The Occupational Outlook Handbook* are two sources for such information. Doing these comprehensive assessments ensures that you have a clear knowledge of the essential tasks of a job for which you are applying, and how your strengths match up with the requirements of the job.

6. Energy patterns (Is there a pattern that's reliable?)

All jobs require differing amounts of energy. Are you a "sprinter" or a "*plodder alonger?*" While those are not real terms, they define the types of people who can either go through each day with the same amount of energy output, or sprint through a job, depleting their energies, and thus feeling "spent." Some people have a pattern to their energy output, while others do not.

To figure out if there is a pattern to your energy output, keep an energy log for 1 or 2 months. Rate yourself on a scale from 1 (very low energy level) to 10 (very high energy level) three times per day—at the beginning, middle, and end of the day. Record these ratings in a log book or day planner (see the What We Know sheet entitled, "Time Management: Learning to Use a Day Planner"). Periodically review the log to see whether there is any pattern in energy level across the day, week, and month. If a pattern is not noticeable, then it will not be difficult to sustain energy at most jobs. However, if a fairly reliable pattern exists, then it may be necessary to learn how to harness energy to do difficult tasks at times when energy is high and do more "automatic" tasks when energy is low or depleted.

7. Workplace habits (what is expected vs. how we measure up)

Job success often depends on personal characteristics, such as dependability, reliability, commitment, and attitude. Consult a career-related book on the reference list for a list of the qualities that employers most often look for in employees. Decide how you measure up to these qualities, and determine whether it is necessary to improve these workplace habits.

8. A complete history of all previous jobs (useful for extracting valuable information)

People learn the most from their mistakes and successes. Look back and explore such things as:

- ♦ What you liked most about each job
- ♦ What you liked least about each job
- ♦ The dates of employment (did you leave after a few months?)

Look for patterns that might help to plan for a future career.

Using the Data

After collecting this data, follow these three steps to maximize the chance of success and minimize the chance of failure:

♦ Read about the jobs you plan to pursue to get a reality check. *The Dictionary of Occupational Titles, Occupational Outlook Handbook,* and related online sources can help give a realistic view of any given job and dispel any fantasies.

♦ Talk to others already doing the job through a series of informational interviews. These will allow you to open your eyes to reality and to "try the career on for size." It's a good idea to speak to three to five people in a given career to get more than one viewpoint.

♦ Observe the job for an hour, a day, or a week, or in a volunteer position. This is the only way to pick up unspoken information, such as how hassled everyone might appear, how well-lit an area is, how calm people seem as they interact with each other, and a host of other almost subliminal factors.

When all of this information has been collected, the following questions can be answered:

♦ What jobs are a "good fit" with my personal strengths, and what jobs are a poor fit?

♦ What fantasies or false beliefs did I have about the jobs I used to think would work well for me?

♦ For the jobs that are a good fit for me, what supportive strategies, accommodations or modifications are necessary to maximize my success?

Conclusion

The suggestions given in this article are commonly used by career counselors who guide adults with AD/HD in dealing with workplace issues. Such suggestions have proven useful for many individuals, but have not yet been subjected to scientific scrutiny. Research is needed to develop a scientifically-based understanding of the problems faced by adults with AD/HD in

the workplace and to evaluate the effectiveness of the kinds of interventions suggested here.

References and Resources

Bolles, R., & Brown, D. (2001). *Job-Hunting for the So-Called Handicapped.* Berkeley, CA: Ten Speed Press.

Brown, D. (2000). *Learning a Living: a Guide to Planning your Career and Finding a Job for People with Learning Disabilities, Attention Deficit Disorder, and Dyslexia.* Bethesda, MD: Woodbine House, Inc.

Dictionary of Occupational Titles. (1993). Washington, DC: U.S. Department of Labor, Employment and Training Administration, U.S. Employment Service.

Fellman, W. (2000). *Finding a Career that Works for You.* Plantation, FL: Specialty Press, Inc.

Latham & Latham. (1994). *Succeeding in the Workplace.* Washington, DC: JKL Communications.

Nadeau, K.G. (1997). *ADD in the Workplace.* Bristol, PA: Brunner/Mazel, Inc.

Occupational Outlook Handbook. (1999-2000). Washington, DC: U.S. Department of Labor, Bureau of Labor Statistics.

Weiss, L. (1996). *ADD on the Job.* Dallas, TX: Taylor Publishing Co.

Web Sites

"The Americans with Disabilities Act: Civil Rights for You," www.ldonline.org/l d_indepth/adult/dale_brown_ada.html

Equal Employment Opportunities Commission, www.eeoc.gov

This information first appeared in the What We Know sheet, "Succeeding in the Workplace," 2003. The information provided in this sheet was supported by Cooperative Agreement Number R04/CCR321831-01 from the Centers for Disease Control and Prevention (CDC). The contents are solely the responsibility of the authors and do not necessarily represent the official views of CDC. It was approved by CHADD's Professional Advisory Board in August 2003.

Managing Money

Managing finances is a unique challenge for an individual with AD/HD. The major features of procrastination, disorganization, and impulsivity can wreak havoc on finances. Because there is no published research concerning financial issues and AD/HD in adulthood, these suggestions are based upon best clinical practices and the application of behavioral and financial principles. This article will discuss:

♦ identifying problem areas with money
♦ organizing financial papers
♦ curbing impulsive spending and the use of credit cards
♦ becoming aware of how money is spent
♦ developing a spending plan and a system to implement the plan
♦ developing a plan to get out of debt and get into the habit of saving

Identify Problem Areas with Money

Most people with money problems believe that not having enough money is their primary problem, and are unable to pinpoint their specific difficulties. Upon further analysis, many adults with AD/HD have one or more of the following specific difficulties:

♦ Bouncing checks, and losing or not paying bills
♦ Impulsive spending or buying things on a whim
♦ Being unable to save for big-ticket items such as new dishwashers, vacations, children's college, or retirement
♦ Losing checks or not keeping track of checkbook balances
♦ Being disorganized with papers, making it impossible to locate them at tax time
♦ Large credit card balances
♦ Procrastinating doing taxes
♦ Forgetting when the car payment or mortgage is due
♦ Not earning enough money for survival (financial underachievement)
♦ Not saving for the future

Establish Short-, Mid- and Long-Term Goals

Once the problem areas are identified, goals for improvement can be set. Individuals with AD/HD need to formulate short-, mid- and long-term goals for improving their finances.

♦ Short-term goals may include such things as cutting up credit cards, saving $5 per week, curbing eating out, or keeping papers together.
♦ Mid-term goals may include saving for a vacation, saving for furniture replacement, or beginning to pay off debts.

♦ Long-term goals may include saving for college tuition or planning for retirement.

Prioritizing these areas poses a special challenge because successful money management means paying attention to all of them. It is advisable to break down each task into small action steps and incrementally build your confidence until you are attending to the whole financial picture.

Organizing Financial Papers

Many individuals with AD/HD get into financial trouble because they lose money, bills and checkbooks, can't find the necessary papers at tax time, or just don't plan. This disorganization is no different than the general disorganization of an individual with AD/HD. However, if lost, financial papers oftentimes have more serious consequences.

To avoid misplacing or losing financial papers, have a special spot in the house where all financial papers can be stored. This can be a file cabinet, desk drawer, special box, large plastic envelope, or a large basket. This central location should be near where the mail is opened, and may also house a calculator, stamps, envelopes, and anything else needed for paying bills.

Daily Mail Routine

It is often helpful to develop a daily routine for opening the mail in a timely manner, particularly money papers. This means that when the mail arrives and is opened, money papers are immediately separated from the rest of the mail and placed into the special container. Money papers include checkbooks, bills, bank statements, legal papers, insurance papers, checks to be cashed, and extra checks. Anything that has a designated account number is important and needs to be immediately separated from the remainder of the papers.

Files with Dividers

Dividers with file names such as *home-related, grocery, gifts, utilities, bank statements, personal, car and fuel, hobbies,* and *insurances* can be placed in the container. These file names should reflect your lifestyle and should be kept simple. Some people find it helpful to color code or label files that are needed at tax time. A sophisticated filing system is not necessary at first—at the very least gather the money papers in one spot. Over time, this organization will become routine.

Paperwork Flow System

A "paperwork flow system" may also be helpful. This is a system in which all the money papers "flow" to one central location. For instance, "temporary holding tanks" are designated in the wallet, purse, planner, and car, which hold money papers and receipts until they can be placed in the special money location. These temporary tanks can be clear plastic envelopes, fancy shoeboxes, plain envelopes, or even more simply, a special spot in the wallet for receipts. Once a month or so, these papers can be transferred to the central location.

Curb Impulsive Shopping

Impulsivity, one of the hallmarks of AD/HD, can lead to financial difficulties. Impulsive shopping and spending is defined as any purchase you did not plan to make when you left the house that morning, any purchase that is not a part of your budget, or any purchase that you don't need. For an adult with AD/HD, this spending happens spontaneously and without warning. Here are suggestions for curbing impulsive spending:

♦ Put an interruption between your money and the urge to spend it. Avoid credit card use and ATM machines. Don't carry your checkbook with you. Consider having

> Many individuals with AD/HD get into financial trouble because they lose money, bills and checkbooks, can't find the necessary papers at tax time, or just don't plan.

another signer on your checking account or not carrying extra cash.

- ♦ Avoid temptations. Identify and stay away from problem areas such as malls, favorite stores, arts and crafts shows, online Web sites, home shopping channels, and newspaper circulars. Throw out catalogs as soon as they arrive.
- ♦ Bring a list when shopping, and stick to it. Before you go to the store, call a friend and commit to your shopping list. When you are done, call them again to report that you have adhered to your list.
- ♦ Bring a calculator to the store to add up purchases as they accumulate.
- ♦ Wait a certain number of hours before a purchase. If this time elapses (say 24 hours) and you decide that you still want the purchase and have the money to buy it, then go and buy it.
- ♦ Find fun hobbies or things to do that are free or inexpensive. Shopping shouldn't be the main pleasure in life. The world is filled with a vast array of stimulating activities for an individual with AD/HD to do. Explore neighborhood museums and libraries, attend local lectures, join support groups or clubs, visit public parks and learn about nature, or participate in sports. Every community has free concerts and live performances. Seek them out.

Cut Up Credit Cards

Credit cards promote impulsive spending; they are easy and convenient to use and very damaging for a person who has a hard time prioritizing financial commitments. The average person spends more when using a credit card rather than cash. If you have large balances on your credit cards and don't remember what you purchased, you would probably be better off without a credit card. Write to the companies and close these accounts even if there are balances to pay off. Credit cards and the debt that can easily accrue can take a person in the wrong financial direction.

Balances build up rapidly from interest, late payment fees, and over the limit charges. This accumulation will rapidly turn small purchases into very large expenses. Paying only the minimum amount due on a large credit card debt means it could take 30 years to pay off the entire balance. If you are in the habit of not paying off credit card balances, the next time you use your credit card, ask yourself if you love the purchase enough to pay for it over 30 years?

More Suggestions for Dealing with Credit Cards

- ♦ Until you are ready to close your accounts, have a trusted friend or loved one hold your card. Writing a check to the credit card company immediately after making a credit card purchase is another temporary solution until you are ready to cut up your card.
- ♦ You can also place a sticker on your credit card that symbolizes some aspect of your vision. This way, when you pull out your credit card, you will be reminded of your longer-term goals, and possibly pause long enough to ask yourself if this purchase is necessary.
- ♦ Some individuals have even kept their credit cards frozen in an ice tray. By the time they defrost the credit card, the urge to make the purchase has often dissipated.

Keeping Records: Becoming Conscious of Where Money is Going

The next step is to keep track of where the money is going. Carry a little notebook and begin to keep track of all purchases. Record even small purchases, such as $.30 for the parking meter or $1.39 for a coffee. Other systems, such as a palm pilot, a calendar, or an extra checkbook register, may suit you better.

Successful money management demands that you be able to *account* for your money. Keeping a record of purchases helps curb impulsivity and serves as an indicator of whether you are spending your money where you want to be spending it—toward the things you love, and toward your vision and values. As spending is tracked, certain categories will naturally emerge. These categories are different for each person, but the main categories for cash include parking, groceries, restaurants, snacks, vending machines, coffee shops, books, gasoline, clothing, newspapers, cosmetics, household items, donations, and hobbies. As you continue to record your spending, you will no longer have to wonder where all the money goes.

It may be difficult for adults with AD/HD to write down all of their expenses, but do the best you can. Try keeping track of expenses for one week or several weeks at first. Enlist the help of a spouse or a trusted friend in writing down all expenses. Try dictating them into a small hand-held recorder or using a cell phone to record expenses as messages on your answering machine. Even if you do not keep a perfect record of every expense, the records that you do collect will help you move forward in changing your money management habits.

Determining Expenses and Developing a Spending Plan

Collecting records of all spending paves the way for the creation of a spending plan. A spending plan is like a budget. It involves allocating a certain amount of money each month for each spending category in your life. Follow the steps below to develop a simple spending plan. Spreadsheet software can be helpful in developing a spending plan.

♦ Make a master list of all expenses. Gather these figures from checkbook records and credit card statements from the past 12 months.

♦ Sum all expenses from the past 12 months and divide by 12 to get the monthly total expenses. For weekly expenses, multiply them by 4.3 to get the monthly amount (there is one third of a week extra per month). It is easier to construct a spending plan monthly rather than annually

since most utilities and installments are paid monthly.

One secret to healthy financial management is to plan for all expenses every single month. For instance, many people with AD/HD have difficulty remembering that the insurance bill is due in 2 months so they impulsively spend or splurge on the latest electronic gadget or a vacation. The impulsive, live-in-the-moment lifestyle of the individual with AD/HD makes it difficult to remember upcoming expenses. The spending plan or budget can help keep these upcoming expenses top of mind, and ensure that they are planned for every month and not forgotten.

> Keeping a record of purchases helps curb impulsivity.

Some suggestions for this:

♦ Use an envelope system. Label a series of envelopes with the names of the major categories of budget items. Upon receiving a paycheck, cash it and place the amount of money allocated for each category in the proper envelope. Whenever an expense needs to be paid, withdraw money from the appropriate envelope. When there is little or no money left in a given envelope, you will know that you have spent the allocated amount for that category and can stop making further purchases in that category until you receive the next paycheck. Using an envelope system ensures that the proper amount for necessities is available when they are due.

♦ Record every monthly expenditure in your checkbook at the beginning of the month so you will know when they are due. It may be helpful to eliminate paper and arrange for utilities, car payments, and house payments to be automatically withdrawn from a bank account.

◆ Special accounts: Open a special bank account for large ticket items and fluctuating categories such as vacations, car repair, clothing, home repair, and replacements, and make a monthly deposit to this account.

◆ Sudden expenses: If you are consistently faced with sudden unexpected expenses such as car repairs, dental and medical emergencies, roof leaks and other household problems, then open a special account for these sudden "emergencies." Remember, most cars break down, teeth need repair and homes need maintenance. They are a predictable part of life so plan ahead for them.

Paying Off Debts

As stated earlier, success with finances demands the elimination of debt and the prevention of new debt. To pay off debt, make a list of all debts that includes credit cards, as well as outstanding debts to doctors, dentists, friends and family, and loans from 401K plans.

If you are in serious debt, this may be an emotionally painful task. Do it anyway. Talk with a trusted friend or therapist to help deal with the emotional pain. Call creditors to ask for a lower percentage rate or reduced late fees. Arrange regular payments with creditors and stick to the plan. Do not promise more than you can realistically pay. They are less likely to cooperate if you don't keep promises or stick to what you have agreed to pay monthly.

Savings

The savings habit should begin immediately, even if it means starting with a piggy bank and making weekly deposits of small amounts, even $.50 or $1.00. No matter how high the debt load, a savings habit needs to be developed. Start small, and be patient with yourself as you learn this new habit. There are different purposes for saving money:

◆ Short-term expenditures: These include items like a new refrigerator, a vacation, or insurance payments due annually or semi-annually.

◆ Mid-term expenditures: These include children's education, a down payment on a new car, or the purchase of a new home.

◆ Long-term future savings: These include retirement. This type of savings is especially difficult for an individual with AD/HD to conceptualize because there is no need in the here and now to be saving. Nevertheless, the day will come when you'll need this money to live on.

The solution for all of these savings needs is to make saving money fun and visual. For instance, some people find it helpful to use a cute piggy bank for certain expenditures; others find it helpful to use an envelope with a photo of whatever you are saving for glued to the outside. You can also open a special bank account for a particular goal and have automatic deposits taken from your paycheck. If necessary, open this bank account at a different bank—across town so you'll be less tempted to withdraw from it. Some also find it helpful to make a visual thermometer or graph as they save money for special occasions.

Find Support and Incorporate Other Resources

Some people may be able to implement the suggestions given here on their own. Others may need the assistance of a friend, therapist, or coach. An individual providing support can help the adult with AD/HD make budget categories and monitor and regulate spending. Those individuals who take medication should make sure that their medication is active in their body when they are working on financial tasks.

Putting Money Management on a Timeline

To manage money effectively, it is necessary to organize the ideas in this article on a timeline. Below is one example of such a timeline, which specifies tasks to be done daily, weekly, monthly, and yearly. The approximate amount of time it might take to accomplish each task is also listed. The reader should create a similar timeline that is customized to his/her own circumstances.

Daily

♦ Place money papers in one central location. (less than 5 minutes)
♦ Open and sort bills. (5 minutes)
♦ Record spending. (less than 5 minutes)
♦ Review vision and budget if over spending. (less than 10 minutes)
♦ Keep a daily account balance on checking accounts. (less than 5 minutes)
♦ Resist impulsive spending.

Weekly

♦ Pay bills; write checks and mail them; mark date paid and move paid bills to folder marked "PAID." (10-20 minutes)
♦ Review expenses for the upcoming week. (5 minutes)
♦ Go to the bank; deposit checks and withdraw needed cash for the week. (20 minutes)
♦ Add up weekly spending, especially in problem categories. (10 minutes)

Monthly

♦ File "PAID" bills into appropriate files. (5-10 minutes)

♦ Reconcile bank statement. (30 minutes)
♦ Compare actual income and spending to budgeted allocations. (5 minutes)
♦ Assess areas of overspending.

Yearly

♦ Collect money papers for tax preparation. (1 hour)
♦ Create a financial vision for the upcoming year. (30 minutes)
♦ List large expenses for the next year. Assess necessary repairs, clothes needed, major gifts, and travel. (10 minutes)
♦ After tax preparation is complete, box up money papers, label with appropriate year, and put in storage. (30 minutes)

Suggested Resources

Dominguez, J., & Robin, V. (1992). *Your Money or Your Life.* New York: Penguin Books, Ltd.

Mundis, J. (1995). *Earn What You Deserve.* New York: Bantam Books.

Mundis, J. (1988). *How to Get Out of Debt, Stay Out of Debt, and Live Prosperously.* New York: Bantam Books.

Tyson, E. (1995). *Personal Finance for Dummies.* Foster City, CA: IDG Books Worldwide, Inc.

The information provided in this article is based on the What We Know sheet, "Managing Money," 2003, and was supported by Cooperative Agreement Number R04/CCR321831-01 from the Centers for Disease Control and Prevention (CDC). The contents are solely the responsibility of the authors and do not necessarily represent the official views of CDC. It was approved by CHADD's Professional Advisory Board in August 2003.

Scott Eyre Finds Relief

by Peg Nichols

It's October 2003 and a month to remember for baseball lovers of all ages. The West Coast Division leader San Francisco Giants are hosting the wild card Florida Marlins in Pacific Park Stadium for game three of the National League Playoffs.

Bottom of the seventh. Score tied at two apiece. Marlins' Miguel Cabrera is on first with two outs when Giants' left-handed relief pitcher Scott Eyre, 31, enters the game. He's calm, focused and ready. His job? Keep Cabrera—or any other Marlin for that matter—from scoring.

Juan Pierre, the Marlins' left-handed center fielder, steps up to the plate. Eyre takes a quiet, calm breath, visualizes what he's going to throw, and then throws it: a 90 mph fastball. Strike one. Next pitch. Eyre repeats the process. With a calm, even breath he pictures the pitch and then delivers: another fastball, 92 mph. Strike two. By now, he's feeling really good. His arm is loose, and his mind is focused. Next pitch: another 92 mph fastball,

this one outside the strike zone. Ball one. He closes his eyes briefly as he pictures his fourth pitch. Steady, smooth and swift, he winds up then delivers a 94 mph fastball. Pierre hits it straight to short, Cabrera is out at second, and the inning is over with Florida no further ahead. Mission accomplished. Eyre leaves the mound, humbled and satisfied, "I did my job."

Life on and off the baseball field hasn't always been this smooth for Eyre who was diagnosed with AD/HD less than two years ago. In fact, for much of his Major League career, which has included time with the Chicago White Sox and Toronto Blue Jays, he has been recognized as a gifted though highly erratic pitcher. "For as long as I can remember, I've always had trouble concentrating and sitting still," says Eyre. "But it never occurred to me until I started taking a closer look at myself that I might actually have a medical condition. Getting diagnosed has changed my life in every imaginable way—it's a whole lot better."

His wife Laura couldn't agree more. "Scott is a great husband and father, but his restlessness, impatience and tendency to interrupt were becoming big problems both at home and with his teammates. I'm proud of Scott for taking responsibility of his health and using his experiences to help others. He seems much happier now, and our family life is much more enjoyable."

The parents of two sons—Caleb, 5, and Jacob, 3—Scott and Laura Eyre jointly decided this past spring to speak publicly about Scott's AD/HD and the impact it has had on their lives. "AD/HD affects everyone in the home, not just the person who has it," Laura Eyre continues. "Now that Scott is taking a stimulant medication and learning new strategies for staying focused, we're all happier."

Some of these strategies include having a clearly defined daily schedule (which Laura helps Scott develop), using a Palm Pilot, completing tasks and requests as soon as they're given, incorporating downtime into his day, and accepting help and feedback from others so that he stays on track.

Was there a defining moment that led Eyre to seek treatment for his AD/HD? "Not really," he says. "It was more like a consecutive string of bad experiences, feedback from my wife, and feedback from my teammates about how I couldn't sit still and couldn't stop talking that got me thinking that something wasn't quite right."

Including a disastrous and humiliating experience on the mound at Yankee Stadium.

"I was playing for the Blue Jays at the time and got called into the game at the top of the seventh inning," recalls Eyre. "I was throwing poorly and felt completely unfocused. The catcher approached me to talk. As he started walking back to home plate, I literally began to panic. I couldn't remember a single word he had just said. All I could hear or see or think about was the noisy stadium, the screaming fan who wanted me out of the game, the lights, the advertisements, the announcer—everything except what I was supposed to be focused on: my pitching.

"Around the same time, one of my teammates (Justin Miller) told me that he had AD/HD. I didn't know much about the condition, but as I listened to him describe his life and reflected back on my experience at Yankee Stadium and other moments just like it, I thought, whoa, that's me. A few days later, I went to our team psychologist, Tim Hewes. I described what my body and mind felt like both on and off the field. After about a 45-minute discussion, he suggested that I see a psychiatrist for a full evaluation.

"So, I saw Dr. Luis Herrero, was diagnosed with AD/HD and began taking stimulant medication the same week. The difference was almost instantaneous. For the first time in my life, I felt like I was in control of my body, instead of it being in control of me. Before I started taking medication, I was distracted by just about everything. For example, I might hear a song on the radio and then it would play repeatedly in my head like a broken record for hours and hours. Or instead of focusing on the batter who was waiting for my pitch, I'd focus on the one noisy fan in the stands.

"I'm really grateful I've been able to put a name on something that kept me down in ways I didn't fully realize. My only regret is that I didn't get diagnosed earlier. I wish I could go back to high school and do it all again—with treatment. Things might have been much different for me in the classroom and at home if I had."

A gregarious person described by friends as "big-hearted and down-to-earth," Eyre showed a keen interest in baseball as early as the age of two. "He learned to swing a bat before he could walk," says his mother Peggy. "He always had a bat in his hands, and every piece of furniture—bed, table, chair—instantly became a surface for hitting a ball, sometimes for hours at a time."

The oldest of six children (five boys and one girl), Eyre spent most of his youth in California, where his hyperactivity was as well known as his talent for baseball. "My dad played amateur softball and spent hours playing catch with us when he got home from work," recalls Eyre. "He loved everything about baseball and passed the love of the game on to me."

Eyre's parents divorced when he was eight, his father moved to an apartment, and his

> Getting diagnosed has changed my life in every imaginable way—it's a whole lot better.

mother raised Scott and four of his siblings on her own. When he was 15, his mother moved the family to Magna, Utah, where other family members lived. "My dad is now an active part of my life, and we've rebuilt our relationship," says Eyre, "but for most of my teenage years, my mom was the one who was there for me."

Quiet, reserved and shy, Peggy Eyre had a profound influence on her son. Eyre describes her as his role model. "Her calmness was comforting. She encouraged me. She believed in me. We didn't have much money, but I never felt deprived. Now that I'm a parent myself, I have an even greater appreciation for everything she did. She didn't judge others and she always encouraged us to give people the benefit of the doubt."

Did she suspect that her son was having attention problems when he was a child? "Not really," says Peggy Eyre. "I certainly recognized Scott's hyperactivity, but because he wasn't disruptive and because no one talked much about AD/HD at the time, I didn't worry about it. Now that I know more about the condition, all of his previous patterns and behaviors make better sense. As a boy and definitely through high school he was impulsive, restless and could fly off the handle over the smallest things. His grades weren't great, but they weren't terrible either. Scott has always been a very likeable person—and a good athlete—so those who encountered him tended to focus on his strengths, not his deficits."

Eyre married a woman much like his mother. Equally quiet, reserved and shy, Laura Eyre brings the same calmness and sense of positive thinking into her husband's world. "She encourages me, believes in me, and helps me stay on track. Laura is the glue that keeps this family together," says Eyre.

When the Giants are on the road, the Eyres speak as often as six times a day by phone. "Even though he might be hundreds of miles away, I always feel connected. It's nice," says Laura. When the Giants are in town, she and the boys go to every game. "I still get nervous

when Scott is pitching, but not nearly as much since he was diagnosed. He used to twitch and fidget on the mound. He'd pull at his shirt collar. I could feel his nervousness from my seat. Now, he's focused. He exudes more confidence. He looks like he's in command of his body."

His stats certainly suggest that he is. The versatile left-hander finished the 2003 season with 3.32 ERA (earned run average)—quite an improvement over his 2002 4.97 ERA. [Note to those not familiar with pitching objectives: the lower the number, the better!]

"Some might attribute the improvement to more experience and maturity," reflects Eyre. "Both certainly play a part, but I believe the real improvement is the result of getting the treatment I needed. Now when I head to the mound, I'm in a completely different mental and physical place."

Bob Fratto, 17-year veteran history teacher at Cyprus High School in Magna, Utah, and Eyre's baseball coach for three years, also notices the difference. "He approaches each pitch with greater control and focus."

Close friends to this day, Fratto marvels, though is not surprised, at the path his former player has taken. "Scott was the most gifted high school baseball player I ever coached. I knew that he wasn't a good student, but his attention problems were never a factor on the field. In fact, he was the best hitter, pitcher and all-around athlete I'd ever worked with—not counting his younger brother Willie." [Eyre's youngest brother Willie, also coached for three years by Fratto, is currently a Minor League player for the Minnesota Twins.]

Following graduation from high school in 1990, Eyre attended Southern Idaho Junior College for a year before the Texas Rangers selected him in the ninth round of the June 1991 draft. Eyre then played for the Chicago White Sox from 1997–2000 and the Toronto Blue Jays during 2001 (bouncing back and forth between their Major and Minor League clubs). He was awarded to the Giants on waiver claim from Toronto at the end of the

2002 season and began proving his stuff during the Giants' 2002 run to the World Series Championship title against the Anaheim Angels.

"There are certain life moments you never forget," says Eyre, who openly describes himself as a sentimental and highly emotional person. One of those moments occurred on August 20, 2001, when Eyre was called up to the Major League team from the Blue Jays Minor League club. "I called my family, got on a plane, headed to Minnesota and took my place in the bullpen. My whole family was there, including my mom and dad. At the bottom of the sixth inning, with two outs, Buck Martinez (then manager) called me into the game. The Metrodome has this really long flight of stairs, and I remember sprinting up them, two at a time, tears in my eyes. I pitched one inning—just did what I was asked to do. After the game, I thanked Martinez. He looked at me and told me something I'll remember to this day, 'When you're playing, you can't control anything except what you do on the field.' I remember his words every time I wind up to pitch."

Fratto was at Eyre's first Major League game and has attended many others since. "For as long as I've known Scott, he's been saying that he wants to accomplish something important. Despite win after win in high school, he's always felt that he needed to do something *more*. I'll always remember his first Major League game, and I'll never forget his performance in the World Series game against Anaheim. How many guys can say that they've played in a Major League baseball game, let alone the World Series? After the game, I said to him, 'So, *now* do you feel like you've accomplished something significant?' He just smiled.

"Scott is everyman. Fame hasn't affected him much. He's good to everyone he meets. He signs autographs after every game and he's never forgotten his roots. Magna is a small, miner's town. Scott didn't have many material possessions growing up. But he had a mom who came to every game, drove him to every practice and supported her kids' love of baseball in whatever way she could. Through her example and the example of others around him, he learned early on what's important in life."

Today Scott Eyre freely shares with the public his experience of living with and getting treatment for AD/HD. "I want kids to know that having AD/HD is nothing to be ashamed of. And I want parents to know how important it is to seek professional help for their child if they suspect attention problems. I only wish I'd been diagnosed sooner."

"That's my son," says Peggy Eyre as she watches Scott on the mound. When asked how she feels about him speaking to others about AD/HD, her pride is obvious. "I think it's great. He's using his life experiences to help others. He's making a difference."

Now if that isn't significant, what is?

> I want kids to know that having AD/HD is nothing to be ashamed of.

Peg Nichols is a former CHADD director of communications and media relations and former executive editor of *Attention!*® magazine.

This article first appeared in *Attention!*® magazine, December 2003.

Just What is Coaching

by Joel L. Young, M.D. and David Giwerc, MCC

AD/HD coaches help clients develop problem-solving skills to cope with their AD/HD, often a valuable complement to medication management.

Many patients and physicians are beginning to realize the value of including an AD/HD coach as a part of the treatment team. Just as an athletic coach motivates an athlete, coaches for AD/HD can help motivate their clients. While therapists are highly educated and licensed professionals, coaching is still an emerging field with no currently recognized educational requirements.

Although AD/HD is generally considered a childhood disorder, at least 67 percent of children with AD/HD continue to exhibit varying degrees of the disorder into adulthood (Barkley, 2001). Some sources claim an even greater prev-alence. In fact, the exact number of adults who have AD/HD remains unknown.

Wender (2000) notes that the negative consequences of AD/HD are greater for adults than for children. While impulsivity in the classroom may only result in a teacher's reprimand, impulsive adult activities may have more serious consequences. Adults with AD/HD are more likely to have driving accidents, license suspensions and speeding tickets. They can be impulsive shoppers, become involved in unwise business activities and may have short-lived romances and marriages. Wender also notes that spouses of adults who have AD/HD feel unheard and unimportant.

In fact, adults who have AD/HD face many unique challenges that are a direct result of their disorder. These include problems with interpersonal relationships, difficulties getting and keeping jobs and other lifelong impairments. The adult who has undiagnosed or untreated AD/HD often does not understand the condition or how it impacts the lives of those who have it.

Better diagnostic techniques and therapeutic interventions have made it easier for physicians to care for patients who have AD/HD. The physician, typically a pediatrician, psychiatrist or primary care doctor, must be comfortable in making the diagnosis. Since research clearly indicates the role of psychopharmacology as an AD/HD intervention, the physician must be proficient in managing any medications used to treat the disorder and any comorbidities present.

Medications can improve focus and reduce other symptoms of AD/HD. However, medications alone cannot teach the patient how to compensate for unlearned life skills. For example, people acquire social skills and "good manners" during childhood. Socially appropriate behaviors are expected to be well established by the time the patient enters adolescence or young adulthood. Unfortunately, the child with AD/HD often does not learn age-appropriate social behaviors, and the gap between expectations and performance continues to widen as the child grows. Socially inappropriate children become socially inappropriate adults, often with unfortunate consequences.

Exploring New Treatment Options for AD/HD

To help address these behavioral components of AD/HD, physicians rely upon other mental health professionals such as psychiatrists, psychologists or clinical social workers. The combined efforts of the clinician and psychotherapist allow greater patient access to the clinician for medical management. This team approach provides the patient with AD/HD with appropriate support for the therapeutic issues that frequently accompany the condition. Surveys of physicians indicate that general practitioners view their role in the care and treatment of patients who have AD/HD as largely supportive in nature and involving close liaison with specialist services (Shaw et al., 2002).

Unfortunately, other important issues such as cognitive restructuring needs, time and stress management, self-esteem and relationship difficulties are often not within the domain of the psychotherapist. AD/HD is not depression (although depression is a common comorbidity among those who have AD/HD). Current research indicates that AD/HD is a brain-based, biological disorder. It is not the result of childhood trauma, post-traumatic stress disorder or other conditions traditionally addressed by psychotherapy. However, while these conditions can and often do exist alongside AD/HD, they are separate from the AD/HD diagnosis.

The patient who has AD/HD also needs practical strategies that will allow him or her to accomplish even mundane daily tasks like getting to work on time, paying bills regularly and learning other basic life skills. Furthermore, adults with AD/HD are often trapped in a frustrating cycle of failure that severely limits their quality of life. One of the hallmarks of AD/HD is the gap between ability and performance. This gap must be closed or reduced if the patient is to enjoy the full benefits of treatment.

The AD/HD Coach

Coaches use highly pragmatic approaches to problem solving, and their use is becoming increasingly popular among high-performance individuals who may or may not wish to use a therapist. The main objective of coaching is to identify what is preventing the client from reaching a specific goal and to work with him or her to create a specific plan for reaching it.

Therapy and coaching are not the same, and the two disciplines are not interchangeable. While therapists are highly educated and licensed professionals, coaching is still an emerging field with no currently recognized educational requirements. Some clients with AD/HD see both a coach and a therapist as part of their personal AD/HD management program.

Coaching completes the bridge between biology and behavior and narrows the gap between ability and performance. Many patients and physicians are beginning to realize the importance of including an AD/HD coach as a part of the treatment team. And for some clients with AD/HD, their coach was the first person to not only understand their frustrations, but to sincerely believe all of their AD/HD stories.

The less formal coach/client connection is more conducive to personal encouragement and motivation than the traditional doctor/patient relationship. Physicians can rarely provide this level of attention and encouragement within the restrictions of the typical office visit. The coach becomes the client's champion, reinforcing and reminding the individual of his or her natural talents and successes.

An AD/HD coach also creates a safe environment that encourages the honest and open

> Adults with AD/HD are often trapped in a frustrating cycle of failure.

communication necessary for behavioral changes to occur. This environment exists on a foundation of unconditional acceptance of the client coupled with science-based instruction about AD/HD. Within such a structure of safety, the coach focuses on identifying and acknowledging the natural talents of the individual and developing a plan to convert them into daily strengths.

> AD/HD coaches help clients develop problem-solving skills and strategies to cope with their AD/HD

Many coaches may also have AD/HD and be intimately familiar with the challenges faced by others with the disorder. Although having AD/HD is not a requirement for being a coach, those who have been diagnosed with the disorder offer their clients a heightened sense of empathy and hope that they, too, can master the challenges associated with the condition.

AD/HD coaches help clients develop problem-solving skills and strategies to cope with their AD/HD, which can be a valuable complement to medication management. In some cases, coaching may be helpful for those who are reluctant to use established forms of treatment, such as psychotropic medications or therapy. While coaching cannot replace stimulant medication as a treatment for AD/HD, a coach can provide some strategies for accommodating to the disorder. Additionally, further education about AD/HD may encourage the patient to pursue medical treatment options. Depending on the specific needs of the patient, the AD/HD coach may also address the benefits of specific lifestyle issues such as proper sleep, nutritional habits and exercise.

Keeping the Client Focused

Patients with AD/HD have a great deal of difficulty maintaining their focus. Medication can help, but there may still be times when focus is minimal at best. The coach helps determine how the client handles different challenging tasks by identifying distinct phases of attending:

1. Focusing on the intended stimulus
2. Sustaining focus
3. Shifting focus at will
4. Hyper-focusing (intense focusing on negative thoughts that can lead to serious reflection)
5. Hypo-focusing or daydreaming (the weakest level of focus presenting the greatest challenge)

Once the various phases have been identified and understood, the coach works with the client to develop strategies that will help maintain focus.

Psychoeducation

Psychoeducation is an integral part of the coaching process. During this phase of the relationship, the coach educates the client about how and where the challenges of AD/HD are manifested in daily life. For example, people with AD/HD tend to be visual thinkers, and coaches are taught to use creative metaphors to help patients visualize the effects of AD/HD on their lives and how to overcome them.

During the psychoeducation phase of coaching, the coach shares information supported by scientific research about AD/HD. The coach uses the documented and proven body of knowledge from reputable and respected sources to explain the client's past inability to perform as a function of undiagnosed and untreated AD/HD, not as a result of being "broken" or having a character flaw. Understanding the effect of AD/HD on the brain and the life of an individual, can diminish—and in many cases eliminate—years of self-blaming behaviors that have contributed to the low self-esteem of the individual and the continued cycle of failure. The client learns that AD/HD is a brain-based disorder with unique strengths, while at the same time emphasizing that AD/HD is not an excuse for past mistakes or other problems.

Professional Regulation and Standards

AD/HD coaching is one of many niches that are part of the profession of personal coaching. There is not a single entity or organization that regulates AD/HD coaching. However, there is one governing body that is responsible for monitoring the integrity of the entire coaching industry (Weiss et al., 1993).

The International Coach Federation (ICF), founded in 1992, is the largest not-for-profit professional association of personal and business coaches, boasting more than 6,000 members and 144 chapters in 30 countries. The ICF (www.coachfederation.org) seeks to preserve the integrity of coaching around the globe and conducts a certification program that helps establish the standard for coaches worldwide.

The purpose of the ICF Credentialing Program is to:

♦ Establish and administer minimum standards for credentialing professional coaches and coach training agencies.
♦ Assure the public that participating coaches and coach training agencies meet or exceed these minimum standards.
♦ Reinforce professional coaching as a distinct and self-regulating profession.

The ICF credentials of Professional Certified Coach (PCC) or Master Certified Coach (MCC) are awarded to professional coaches and coach-training agencies able to validate that they meet or exceed these minimum standards.

AD/HD coaches who seek either of these credentials must meet ICF's standards.

Skills and Training

The AD/HD coach who wants to gain the essential skills to effectively coach individuals with AD/HD should enter a training organization that not only meets ICF standards and competencies, but also provides a comprehensive understanding of AD/HD's challenges and the strategies that can be developed and employed to overcome them.

Currently there are not enough well-trained coaches who have the necessary understanding of AD/HD, its challenges and the skills required to effectively coach the large number of adults with AD/HD requesting these services. Clients should always check references from previous clients, ask prospective coaches about their training and certification and inquire about their knowledge of AD/HD. They can also ask coaches if they have an ICF credential and how long they have had it. ICF-credentialed coaches are required to maintain their designation by meeting specific educational requirements that must be documented and submitted to the ICF (recertification is necessary every three years).

When selecting a coach, the ICF offers the following recommendations:

♦ Individuals should educate themselves about coaching. Hundreds of articles have been written about it in the last three to five years.
♦ They should know their objectives for working with a coach.
♦ They should interview three coaches before deciding on one. Ask about their experience, qualifications and skills, and get at least two references.
♦ Coaching is an important relationship. There should be a connection between the individual and the coach that feels right.

AD/HD coaches support their clients in developing a comprehensive understanding of both the nature and impact of AD/HD. Coaches who have the knowledge and ability to develop effective and customized strategies can augment the services provided by physicians and therapists.

Coaching builds hope by educating clients about their own AD/HD. Through the coaching process, clients gain an understanding that the source for many of their challenges is their disorder, not personal shortcomings. The clients' talents, which are their natural recurring patterns of success, become the foundation for effective systems and strategies that can dramatically improve their quality of life.

References

Barkley, R.A., Fischer, M., Fletcher, K., and Smallish, L. (2002). The persistence of attention-deficit/hyperactivity disorder in young adulthood as a function of reporting source and definition of disorder. *Journal of Abnormal Psychology,* 111, 279–89.

Shaw, K.A., Mitchell, G.K., Wagner, I.J., & Eastwood, H.L. (2002). Attitudes and practices of general practitioners in the diagnosis and management of attention-deficit/hyperactivity disorder. *Journal of Pediatrics and Child Health. Oct; 38,* 481–86.

Weiss, G. & Hechtman, L.T. (1993). *Hyperactive children grown up: 2nd ed.* New York: Guilford Press.

Wender, P. H. (2000). *ADHD: Attention-deficit hyperactivity disorder in children and adults.* New York: Oxford University Press.

Joel L. Young, M.D., is the medical director of the Rochester Center for Behavioral Medicine in Rochester Hills, Michigan. He is board certified by the American Board of Psychiatry and Neurology and holds added qualifications in geriatric, forensic and adolescent psychiatry. Dr. Young has authored many articles about AD/HD and related disorders and served as primary investigator in many recent AD/HD and antidepressant medication field trials.

David Giwerc, MCC, International Coach Federation, is the founder/president of the ADD Coach Academy, a comprehensive AD/HD coach-training program. Giwerc is the president of the Board of Directors of Attention Deficit Disorder Association (ADDA). He was the producer and co-director of the AD/HD Coaching video and has been a featured speaker at ADDA, CHADD and International Coach Federation conventions.

This article first appeared in *Attention!*® magazine, December 2003.

Fostering Resilience

by Robert B. Brooks, Ph.D., and Sam Goldstein, Ph.D.

Mindsets are a set of assumptions or attitudes that we possess about others and ourselves that influence our behaviors and the skills we develop. In this article we review how the prominent characteristics of adults with attention-deficit/hyperactivity disorder (AD/HD), which are evident since childhood and a product of both inborn temperament and life experiences, shape their mindsets. While we will cite research to support our viewpoint, our perspective is influenced significantly by our interactions with countless children and adults we have seen in more than 50 years of combined clinical practice and the many adults with AD/HD who have attended our workshops and conferences and shared their life stories with us.

The Characteristics of Adults with AD/HD

Individuals with the diagnosis of AD/HD are not a homogeneous group. We do not wish to imply that all adults with this diagnosis share an identical mindset. The cognitive style, thoughts and behaviors that contribute to adults being diagnosed with AD/HD, do not define their entire functioning or existence. Nor do we wish to suggest that particular features of this mindset are absent in adults who do not meet the criteria for a diagnosis of AD/HD. However, we believe there are certain core behaviors that many adults with AD/HD display that distinguish them to a greater or lesser degree from individuals without AD/HD. These behaviors elicit responses

from others, responses that contribute to the formation of their mindset. Unfortunately, in far too many instances the mindset of individuals with AD/HD is filled with negativity. The following represent a selected list of behaviors that we believe have some of the strongest impact on their lives.

- Impulsivity
  One of the most prominent characteristics of individuals with AD/HD is their impulsivity and disinhibition.[1] They may rush through tasks, fail to demonstrate social skills by saying or doing things that others experience as abrasive or engage in risky activities. They act before they think, not giving adequate consideration to the consequences of their behaviors.

- Low frustration tolerance
  Closely linked to an impulsive style is how quickly adults with AD/HD report in clinical settings feeling frustrated and angry.[2] If a task is difficult and uninteresting to them, they are prone to give up or blame others. If someone doesn't respond to what they want, they are quick to show their anger.

- Moodiness
  Many adults with AD/HD are burdened by fluctuations in mood. One moment they may feel happy only to feel sad a few moments later. As with any affective disorder, most likely both biology and environment interact to differing degrees with each individual to contribute to the moodiness and depression.[3, 4]

Individuals with AD/HD burdened with low self-esteem typically attribute success to factors outside of their control.

○ Disorganization

One of the most frequent complaints we hear about individuals with AD/HD is their difficulty in becoming organized.[2,5] They lose things, forget where they placed their keys, cannot locate bills to pay, neglect to jot down an important appointment in their book, or fail to complete a project at work because they have misjudged the time required or become distracted with other projects.

○ Rigidity and inflexibility.

The other side of the coin of impulsivity and disorganization is a lack of flexibility, a behavior indicative of a deficit in executive functioning.[6,7] On the one hand, this rigidity may exemplify, in part, a desperate attempt to cope with the disorganization and lack of control in one's life, but it also seems to be another example of a failure of self-regulation.

○ A dearth of empathy

Individuals with AD/HD often demonstrate a limited capacity for empathy. They have difficulty understanding the perspective of others. They are unable to realistically assess and appreciate the "social scene." Their interpersonal relations are frequently filled with tension and a lack of satisfaction. Problems with empathy may be linked with the antisocial personality disorders that have been reported with many adults with AD/HD.[8,9,10]

The Unfortunate Mindset of Adults with AD/HD

The characteristics we have just described will affect almost all aspects of a person's life, frequently resulting in a negative mindset with the following beliefs:

"I do not have a great deal of control of my life."

One of the hallmarks of a positive mindset is feeling a sense of control over what occurs in one's life together with a realistic appraisal of those areas over which one has control and those that are beyond one's sphere of influence.[11,12] The characteristics of AD/HD contribute to a feeling of not being in control.

"When I am successful it is based on luck or chance."

Related to this first characteristic, research indicates that in contrast to adults with high self-esteem, individuals with AD/HD burdened with low self-esteem typically attribute success to factors outside of their control such as luck, chance or fate. Possessing this belief, it is difficult for them to feel confident about experiencing success in the future.[13]

"Failure indicates my inadequacy as a person."

Adults with high self-esteem typically believe that mistakes are experiences to learn from rather than feel defeated by them. Mistakes are attributed to variables that can be modified.[13,14] However, individuals with AD/HD are vulnerable to thinking that they cannot correct the situation or overcome the obstacle. They begin to believe that regardless of what they do, few, if any, positive outcomes will appear. They expect to fail and, thus, retreat from the challenges at hand.

"I'm less worthy than others."

If one encounters many failure situations, it is easy to understand how self-esteem is adversely affected. Self-doubts appear early in the lives of many children with AD/HD and continue into their adulthood.[15]

"The world is unfair."

Individuals with AD/HD often believe that situations and people are unfair. They harbor constant complaints about employers, spouses and salespeople who they believe are unfair. While at times there may be justification to these complaints, frequently they represent anger at feeling misunderstood and not having their demands met.

"I have little, if anything, to offer the world." A sense of self-esteem and dignity is nurtured when individuals feel that they are making a contribution to their world and that their actions make a positive difference. Many adults with AD/HD do not feel they contribute anything positive, as captured in the following comment offered by a man with AD/HD: "I think the only thing I have ever given others is heartache."[15]

Steps for Changing Negative into Positive Mindsets

Ongoing research is clearly warranted to define and articulate the concept of resilience. Fortunately, during the past 10–15 years we have witnessed an increasing number of researchers engaged in the task of studying this concept.[14, 16, 17, 18, 19, 20, 21, 22] As clinicians, one of our main roles when working with individuals with AD/HD who are burdened by a negative mindset and accompanying self-defeating coping behaviors is to help them replace their negative feelings and thoughts with an optimistic, positive outlook and more adaptive ways of managing stress and pressure. The following are steps to assist in this process.

1. Demystifying mindsets

An initial step in changing negative mindsets is to help individuals define and understand (a) the assumptions that they have about themselves (including their AD/HD) and others and (b) how these assumptions prompt certain behaviors and coping strategies that may be self-defeating. We emphasize that mindsets are not set in stone and can be modified.

2. Defining the main components of a positive, resilient mindset.

In many ways the features of a positive mindset are the mirror image of the earlier description of a negative mindset. They include:[14, 16]

- "I will learn to distinguish what I have control over from that which I do not. I will focus my time and energy on those things over which I have control since I am the author of my own life."

- "Success can be based on my own strengths and resources." [This feature of a resilient mindset is closely aligned with feeling a sense of control over one's life.]

- "I believe that mistakes are opportunities for learning and growth." [People are not particularly thrilled when they make mistakes or fail, but when mistakes are viewed as situations from which to learn, people are more willing to take realistic risks rather than backing away from challenges.]

- "I have "islands of competence." [We all have areas of strength or what we call "islands of competence." However, as we have seen, a number of adults with AD/HD fail to acknowledge or appreciate their strengths. This is why we directly ask our clients to tell us what they view as their strengths and how they use these strengths in their daily lives.]

- "I make a positive difference in the world." [A basic component of emotional well-being is the belief that one's actions benefit others. We have witnessed countless examples of individuals, many with AD/HD, who engage in activities that make a positive difference (for example, being involved in a charity, serving as a

> A number of adults with AD/HD fail to acknowledge or appreciate their strengths.

♦ Articulate both short-term and long-term goals for change
♦ Select a couple of goals
♦ Develop realistic, achievable plans to reach the designated goals
♦ Have criteria for evaluating the success of a plan of action
♦ Consider possible obstacles
♦ Change the goals or approach if repeated efforts at success do not work
♦ As goals are reached, add new goals to reinforce a positive mindset and be aware of the negative thoughts that may serve as obstacles to future growth
♦ As new goals are added, continue to develop more effective ways of coping that will help to maintain a positive mindset and strengthen the gains that have been made

Adults with AD/HD are more vulnerable to developing negative mindsets than their counterparts who do not have this condition. An understanding of the components of both negative and positive mindsets can serve as the foundation for developing and implementing strategies that will replace a negative mindset with one of optimism and promise. While such a task of changing mindsets can seem daunting at times, the benefits of leading a more satisfying and resilient life are well worth the effort.

Notes

[1]Barkley, R. (1995). *Taking Charge of AD/HD: The Complete, Authoritative Guide for Parents.* New York, N.Y.: Guilford Press.

[2]Hallowell, E. & Ratey, J. (1994). *Driven to Distraction.* New York, N.Y.: Pantheon Books.

[3]Millstein, R.B., Wilens, T.E., Biederman, J. & Spencer, T.J. (1997). Presenting AD/HD symptoms in subtypes in clinically referred adults with AD/HD. *Journal of Attention Disorders,* 2:159–166.

[4]Rucklidge, J.J. & Kaplan, B.J. (1997). Psychological functioning of women identified in adulthood with attention deficit hyperactivity disorder. *Journal of Attention Disorders,* 2:167–176.

coach in a youth sports league or helping at a senior citizen center). In the process of making and acknowledging this positive difference, a person's sense of dignity and self-worth is enhanced and the roots of a resilient mindset are secured.]

3. Developing a plan of action for change. Once clinicians help adults with AD/HD gain a clearer picture of what AD/HD involves and once the adults can appreciate the assumptions that characterize their mindsets and guide their behaviors, the next step is to articulate a problem-solving model for change. The following model is based on a problem-solving program developed by psychologist Myrna Shure[23, 24] for children and adolescents and is equally relevant for adults. Our modification of Shure's basic model includes the following components, all of which we believe are realistic and achievable.

[5]Solden, S. (2002). *Journeys through ADDdulthood*. New York, N.Y.: Walker & Co.

[6]Gansler, D.A., Fucetola, R., Krengel, M., Stetson, S., Zimering, R. & Makary, C. (1998). Are there cognitive subtypes in adult AD/HD? *Journal of Nervous and Mental Disease, 186*:776–781.

[7]Holdnack, J.A., Noberg, P.J., Arnold, S.E., Gur, R.C. & Gur, R.E. (1995). Speed of processing in verbal learning deficits in adults diagnosed with AD/HD. *Neuropsychiatry, Neuropsychology and Behavioral Neurology, 8*:282–292.

[8]Biederman, J., Faraone, S., Spencer, T., Wilens, T., Norman, D., Lapey, K.A., Mick, E., Lehman, B.K. & Doyle., A. (1993). Patterns of psychiatric comorbidity, cognition and psychosocial functioning in adults with attention deficit hyperactivity disorder. *American Journal of Psychiatry, 150*:1792–1798.

[9]Robin, A.L., Bedway, M. & Tzelepis, A. (1998). Understanding the personality traits of adults with AD/HD: A pilot study. *Attention!®, 4*(4):49–55.

10   Tzelepis, A., Schubner, H. & Warbasse, L.H. (1995). Differential diagnosis in psychiatric comorbidity patterns in adult AD/HD. In K. Nadeau (Ed.), *A Comprehensive Guide to Attention Deficit Disorder in Adults: Research, Diagnosis and Treatment*. (pp. 35–57). New York, N.Y.: Brunner/Mazel.

[11]Gerber, P.J. (2001). Employment of adults with learning disabilities and AD/HD: Reasons for success and implications for resilience. *AD/HD Report, 9*:1–5.

[12]Gerber, P.J., Ginsberg, R. & Reiff, H.B. (1992). Identifying alterable patterns in employment success for highly successful adults with learning disabilities. *Journal of Learning Disabilities, 25*:475–487.

[13]Brooks, R. (2002). Changing the mindsets of adults with AD/HD: Strategies for fostering hope, optimism and resilience. In S. Goldstein & A. Teeter (Eds.), *Clinician's Guide to Adult AD/HD: Assessment and Intervention*. (pp. 127–146). San Diego, Calif.: Academic Press.

[14]Brooks, R. & Goldstein, S. (2004). *The Power of Resilience: Achieving Balance, Confidence and Personal Strength in Your Life*. New York, N.Y.: Contemporary Books.

[15]Brooks, R. (1999). Fostering resilience in exceptional children: The search for islands of competence. In V. Schwean & D. Saklofske (Eds.), *Handbook of Psychosocial Characteristics of Exceptional Children*. (pp. 563–586). New York, N.Y.: Kluwer Academic/Plenum Press.

[16]Brooks, R. & Goldstein, S. (2001). *Raising Resilient Children*. New York, N.Y.: Contemporary Books.

[17]Goldstein, S. & Brooks, R. (Eds.) (2004). *Handbook of Resilience in Children*. New York, N.Y.: Kluwer Academic Publishers.

[18]Katz, M. (1996). *On Playing a Poor Hand Well*. New York, N.Y.: Norton.

[19]Reivich, K. & Shatte, A. (2002). *The Resilience Factor*. New York, N.Y.: Broadway Books.

[20]Seligman, M.E.P. (1990). *Learned Optimism: How to Change Your Mind and Your Life*. New York, N.Y.: Pocket Books.

[21]Seligman, M.E.P. (2002). *Authentic Happiness*. New York, N.Y.: Free Press.

[22]Werner, E. & Smith, R. (1992). *Overcoming the Odds: High Risk Children from Birth to Adulthood*. Ithaca, N.Y.: Cornell University Press.

[23]Shure, M.B. (1994). *Raising a Thinking Child*. New York, N.Y.: Holt.

[24]Shure, M.B. (2000). *Raising a Thinking Preteen*. New York, N.Y.: Holt.

Robert Brooks, Ph.D., is a member of the faculty at Harvard University and a former member of the CHADD Professional Advisory Board. Sam Goldstein, Ph.D., is a member of the faculty at the University of Utah and serves on the *Attention!®* Editorial Advisory Board. Together they have authored seven books, including their recent text, *The Power of Resilience* (Contemporary, 2004).

This article first appeared in *Attention!®* magazine, October 2004.

Finding His Rhythm: Jazz Vocalist Phillip Manuel Talks about Life with AD/HD

By Peg Nichols

As one of the country's leading jazz vocalists, New Orleans native Phillip Manuel is accustomed to traveling around the world. But it wasn't until he was diagnosed in 2000 with AD/HD—at the age of 46—that his life journey began to make much sense to him.

"I don't even remember the person I was four years ago," says Phillip. "Receiving a diagnosis, getting treatment, and learning more about myself and how I relate to others has changed my life in ways I never imagined were possible."

Born into a family of singers, dancers and instrumentalists in the nation's jazz capitol,

Phillip has been surrounded by and immersed in music his entire life. He was singing long before he was speaking full sentences in a household filled with song. "My dad had, without a doubt, the most beautiful voice I've ever heard. My happiest memories include singing with my dad, his brothers, sisters and cousins. Everybody had their own song while we all sang background."

Phillip first performed publicly at the age of 11, was paid $50, and—in his own words—never looked back. As a teen, he sang with a number of local bands and at 16, he made his first record. In 1981, at 28, he was asked to produce and sing the soundtrack for the movie, "Cane River," being filmed in Louisiana. He received rave reviews—a rising star, poised for success.

But there were parts of Phillip's life that were far from harmonious.

His parents divorced when he was four years old, and his relationship with his mother—with whom he lived, along with his grandmother—was continually fraught with tension. "My mother and I have always had a difficult relationship," states Phillip. "No one knew about AD/HD back then, so it never occurred to her that maybe I was having problems for reasons I couldn't control."

As for his father, Phillip maintained a close rapport following the divorce. However, his dad had big challenges of his own. He was an alcoholic and suffered from debilitating anxiety. "I don't think I've ever met anyone as fearful as him. He rarely leaves his home. He refused to see a doctor for almost 30 years. Several years ago, he developed such a bad infection in his legs, he had to have them both amputated," says Phillip. "However, my dad is my soul mate. He never sat me down for life lessons, but I understand tenderness and intimacy because of the way he was with me. I have an appreciation for subtlety, understatement and things sublime because of how he sang to me. He is my greatest example of integrity and a pure heart."

Memories—colorful, vibrant memories—come easily to Phillip. "When I was a boy, my grandmother and I would sit on her bed—just the two of us—watching the Andy Williams show every Saturday night. He was one of my first vocal influences, and it's one of my fondest memories with her."

Always a free spirit, Phillip's inattention and impulsivity became apparent when he went to school. He was rambunctious and, at the drop of a hat, could and would explode with rage. He was easily distracted and had a hard time staying focused. At the same time, he had the ability to make people laugh—though in the classroom, it often cost him dearly. "I was the first grader who asked Sister Therese Marie if nuns were bald beneath their habits. Every kid wondered; I asked. I distinctly remember just blurting out the question."

His report cards consistently stated the same thing, "Inattentive in class. Disruptive. Talks back. Underachiever." In ninth grade, Phillip was expelled from his Catholic high school due to an excessively long list of behavioral infractions, capped off by a disruptive outburst in class following the announcement that Martin Luther King, Jr. had been shot.

Yet despite a rocky school history, he never once doubted his intelligence—or his voice. "I doubted a lot of things in life, but my intelligence and ability to sing were two things I never questioned."

"English was my favorite subject," Phillip states with a smile. "I've always loved words. Still do. I remember writing a paper on breeding tropical fish. It was a good paper. I was proud of it, and I got an A. Looking back, I think my English teacher, Ms. Plicque, understood me. That really helped. Math, on the other hand, was my nemesis. Charts and graphs always gave me the blues."

Blessed with his beautiful voice and equally inspiring sense of humor, Phillip made it through high school, though just barely. "I was well liked and had a way of making people laugh. And I was always singing. I sang at talent shows, in the high school choir, and I even sang in class when I wasn't supposed to. Even the nuns, who didn't care much for me or my behavior, knew I had a gift. But I know I was a chore for my teachers—especially in high school."

After high school, Phillip briefly went to college but quickly dropped out. Following his older brother, he joined the Air Force, got married and had a baby almost simultaneously. Upon discharge four years later, he held a series of jobs, all while trying to launch a music career in New Orleans. He worked for three months at the post office. He worked for a small marketing company, doing quite well, until one day—bam—he was fired. He supported himself through singing gigs. His marriage was failing, he and his wife divorced, and Phillip got sole custody of his son, Kris.

And that's when Janice—his wife for the past 25 years—entered his life.

> His report cards consistently stated the same thing, 'Inattentive in class. Disruptive. Talks back. Underachiever.'

Introduced to Phillip by her cousin—then Phillip's music manager and attorney—Janice was not immediately smitten with the ebullient singer. But she was definitely intrigued and moved by his passion for life and his devotion to his young son. "I was on a professional track when we first met," recalls Janice who holds a master's degree in urban planning. "Children were an oddity to me at the time. Yet I immediately sensed Phillip's strong connection to family and his commitment as a single father to raising his five-year-old. He was completely at ease with children, and his openness, spontaneity and sense of joy drew me to him."

The two began dating and 10 months later married. In time, they had two sons of their own—now 15 and 20. Janice's job required substantial travel when the boys were young, so Phillip—whose singing gigs took place primarily at night—took care of most of the daytime activities. He cleaned. He cooked. He fixed things around the house. He took his boys to school every day, and ironically—considering how much he had hated his own school years—he was the primary "homework helper." Phillip says, however, that while his kids were at school, he often lacked the focus to accomplish much. He had fleeting day jobs, but for the most part, he was at home, filling his day with mindless activities—restless and depressed at the same time.

As for his music career, Phillip certainly had the talent to fly, but something stopped him from being able to soar. He continued performing, achieving recognition not only in New Orleans, but also among an increasingly wide jazz circle. From Trinidad to Istanbul, Paris to San Sebastian, he performed and dazzled with his incredible voice. Fellow performers included such greats as Patti Labelle, Aaron Neville, Fats Domino, Ellis Marsalis, Phyllis Hyman and Nicholas Payton. He was nominated for a "Big Easy" award as best actor for his performance in *Williams and Walker*, a musical drama about the life of vaudevillian, Bert Williams.

By all accounts, things seemed to be going well. Yet, something wasn't right.

"Despite outward appearances, I felt like a failure in enormously big ways," Phillip reflects with both sadness and regret. "I wasn't *unhappy* with my life. Janice and the kids brought me—and continue to bring me—tremendous joy. But there was an inexplicable agitation within that kept me at a psychological distance from others. I began to wonder if I really cared about other people. The outside world saw one Phillip Manuel, but I felt as if the real me was trapped and couldn't emerge. There was a real disconnect—one I was aware of—and one I couldn't seem to shake."

And then there were other little problems that, while certainly not life threatening, weren't exactly life enhancing either. Such as his tendency to lose things. A leather coat. A cherished London Fog wind-breaker. A gold ring. Countless pairs of reading and sun-glasses. Checkbooks. Keys. Umbrellas. The list goes on.

By the late 1990s, Phillip's moodiness was becoming more noticeable. He was prone to angry outbursts over the smallest issues, and he couldn't stay focused on anything. He was restless, impatient, fidgety and anxious. "I was well aware that I wasn't always easy to be around—sometimes I was downright mean," says Phillip. "But I didn't know what was driving it. Even worse, I didn't know how to stop it."

Janice was also becoming concerned. Described by others as steady, grounded and even-tempered, her own internal worry about Phillip continued to grow. One day a close friend was describing a cousin who recently had been diagnosed with AD/HD. As Janice listened, the description sounded just like Phillip. So she did some Internet research and came upon CHADD. She downloaded and printed some 35 pages of information for her husband and left it by the bedside. It sat there for several weeks, untouched. Janice decided not to bug him.

They were bickering a lot during this time, typically over inconsequential things—for example, "how to cook an egg."

Phillip typically did the morning cooking. But one day, Janice was fixing the eggs. Phillip came into the kitchen, took one look, and let the criticisms begin to flow like a mighty river. She hadn't heated the skittle correctly. She cracked the shell the wrong way. And as for the way she cooked them, forget it.

Today they can laugh about it, and in time the egg story—for reasons that are later explained—became symbolic of a transformation about to take place. "Eggs obviously were not the issue," Janice states. "But we didn't know how to talk about the things that really mattered."

Phillip eventually began reading the CHADD information. And a light went on. One day, he admitted to Janice—without a trace of defensiveness—that he saw himself in the material. A few weeks later, after finding a specialist known for treating AD/HD in adults, he underwent a comprehensive evaluation—including a 700 question self survey, interviews with members of his family, a comprehensive medical history and even a review of his old report cards.

This led to a diagnosis of AD/HD, along with anxiety disorder and depression. "When the doctor asked me to guess where I was on a scale of 1–10, with 10 being the most severe form of AD/HD, I told him about six or seven."

"How about an eight or a nine?" the doctor responded.

Phillip began taking medication for his disorders and simultaneously began psychotherapy, a regimen he maintains today.

In 2000—the true turning point in his life because of his diagnosis and treatment—Phillip's music career really began to take off.

His CD, *Love Happened to Me,* was released to widespread acclaim. The *New Orleans Times Picayune* wrote, "Phillip's rich, elegant voice braids with the other instruments in a colorful tapestry. Arms outstretched, voice floating like a butterfly in a sun-dappled garden, Phillip allows himself to be carried away by emotion."

National Public Radio stated that his "rich, coffee-dark vocals are in the tradition of romantic crooners such as Billy Eckstine and Nat King Cole. He revels in and examines each textual and melodic nuance like a jeweler examining a fine diamond." After a performance in San Francisco, the *San Francisco Chronicle* declared, "Phillip sang the wordless melody as if it were a prayer."

> With a diagnosis, medication and counseling, I have come to recognize my moods and behaviors for what they are.

Music isn't the only area of Phillip's life that began to take flight. Today, he is the creative director of Bright Moments, a public relations firm that does work for everyone from political candidates to Popeyes® Chicken to the city of New Orleans. He writes and develops marketing campaigns, and his speaking voice is regularly requested for television and radio commercials.

His relationships have changed, too. Recently, Phillip and Janice had a heated argument about whether the entire family would drive their son back to college. Phillip had work to do at the office, but Janice felt that the entire family should make the journey together. But unlike in previous arguments, Phillip retreated, took time to consider the importance of Janice's request and saw how much it meant to her to travel as a family. He also knew that taking his son to school—as opposed to going into the office— was the right choice. He called her and said he would go.

"It was a remarkable turning point for us, well, for me, mostly," Phillip reflects. "For the first time in a long time, we weren't arguing about eggs, so to speak. Instead, we were having a heated discussion about something that mattered—us! And the good news is that we both listened, we compromised, and made it work. Janice is an amazing human being," he says, "She's loved me right through to the other side."

Janice, in turn, marvels at her husband's resiliency, his ability to love and his capacity to forgive. "He's happy," she says. "We're happy."

"With a diagnosis, medication and counseling, I have come to recognize my moods and behaviors for what they are. The AD/HD feeds my anxiety, and my anxiety returns the favor. Through therapy, I've learned how to be a better listener. I try very hard to be a gentleman, to judge less and to love more. I'm definitely a work in progress."

As he gets ready to leave, he smiles and then adds, "But aren't we all?"

Peg Nichols is a former CHADD director of communications and media relations and former executive editor of *Attention!*® magazine.

This article first appeared in *Attention!*® magazine, December 2004.

Medication Management for Adults with AD/HD

by Philip J. Parker, M.D.

Attention-deficit/hyperactivity disorder (AD/HD) is a mental disorder that often lasts from childhood into adulthood. Medication is an integral part of treatment for adults. Medication alone does not always help a person do a better job with problems such as disorganization, managing time, deciding what is most important or just coping with life. But proper medication helps the symptoms of AD/HD—such as not being able to concentrate or control unwanted behavior—and allows an adult to learn important skills he or she needs to succeed in life.

A health professional cannot tell at first which medication will help which patient the most. You may have to try several medications before you find the one—or the combination—that works best for you.

Stimulants

Stimulants are a group of drugs that change the way the brain's chemical messages get from some brain cells to others. They are the first kind of medication a doctor usually tries when treating AD/HD in both children and adults.

The two stimulants most commonly used are called *methylphenidate* (MPH) and *amphetamines* (AMP). The government controls their availability because people could abuse them if they are not used the way a doctor prescribes them.

Several things influence the way a person reacts to stimulant medication: how much medication is taken, how much medication gets into the bloodstream, and how the amount of medication changes the blood levels.

There is no reason to choose one kind of stimulant over the other for someone who has not yet tried either. Both forms of medications—MPH and AMP—affect the brain somewhat differently, so they probably affect people differently.

If you don't do well on one kind of stimulant, you and your doctor will most likely try the other. The medication and the amount taken must match each person's individual needs.

Talk to your doctor about what side effects you might have with the stimulant he or she prescribes. Side effects of stimulants in adults are generally not serious. They may include one or more of the following: trouble sleeping, headaches, anxiety, loss of appetite and weight loss. Sometimes there are heart rate or blood pressure side effects.

> You may have to try several medications before you find the one—or the combination—that works best for you.

Nonstimulant Medications

Most nonstimulant medications generally aren't used to treat AD/HD unless stimulants don't help or a patient has another psychiatric illness that would become worse if stimulants were used.

Atomoxetine is a new, nonstimulant for people with AD/HD. Its side effects—which are often mild and may go away during treatment—

Four Ways Adults can be Proactive in Medication Management

by Robert M. Tudisco, Esq.

The success of your diagnosis and treatment depends on your active participation. Consider the following tips to maximize the effectiveness of your medication plan.

- ♦ **Be Captain of Your Healthcare Team**
  Remember that you are the common denominator. It is important that your primary care physician be in the loop with your mental health care provider and that you encourage regular communication between them.
- ♦ **Keep a Medication Diary**
  time you spend with your treating doctor is a relatively small slice of your life. Observations made on a daily basis, by you and those around you, will help your doctor tailor your prescription to your particular needs.
- ♦ **Be Patient and Keep an Open Mind**
  In many instances a co-existing condition can impact your response to medication. It is important that your doctor uncover other health issues that may affect your response to medication in order to determine the best course of treatment.
- ♦ **Be Realistic about Your Medication**
  Medication is not a cure for AD/HD, but can help manage its symptoms. Behavioral supports are also important. Think of medication as a useful tool that helps you make positive changes in your life.

Being an active partner with your health care providers can make your treatment of AD/HD more effective. It can also go a long way toward empowering you to retake control of your life.

Robert M. Tudisco, Esq., is a practicing attorney and adult diagnosed with AD/HD. He is a member of Attention!" magazine's Editorial Advisory Board and a member of the 2005-08 CHADD Board of Directors. He has researched and written extensively on adult coping mechanisms and legal and advocacy issues. He welcomes questions and comments at his Web site, www.ADDcopingskills.com.

include dry mouth, insomnia, nausea, constipation, loss of appetite, dizziness, decreased sexual interest and performance and problems with urination. It also may have heart and blood pressure side effects. Potential liver damage has recently been identified as a serious side effect. Atomoxetine appears to work as well as stimulants.

Antidepressants

Antidepressants are medications that help treat depression, but some also seem to help with the symptoms of AD/HD. The reverse is also true: some antidepressants may actually make AD/HD symptoms worse. There are different types of antidepressants, and each works somewhat differently.

Choosing a Medication

It is very important to match your individual needs with what a medication will probably do—or not do—for your symptoms. For a long time, stimulants have been the best medications to try first. You and your health professional must think about both the benefits and the possible side effects of any medication you try.

For example, an adult may have very serious AD/HD symptoms, which could cause him or her to lose a job, and a problem with high blood pressure. With help from a health professional, this adult may choose a medication for AD/HD that is helpful during the workday, but does not cause blood pressure problems.

Keeping Track of the Effects of Medication

It is important to know how well your medication works over time. Keeping track of how you react to your medication takes a lot of effort. The effort is worth it because you and your healthcare professional will then know when it is best to take the medication and how much you should take. It will help you both decide if you need other medications or if, for example, you need more help with problem behavior. You may need coaching, tutoring or counseling in addition to the medication.

Improving Quality of Life

Treating the basic symptoms of AD/HD is very important, but it is often not the only goal of treatment. Treatment can also help you with problems you have in the real world. It can help you be more self-sufficient and to better cope with the demands of everyday life.

Conclusion

Problems with AD/HD can continue after childhood. Medication is the basic part of treatment. Psychostimulants are usually the medications tried first, but many nonstimulant treatments are available, too. Medications can help most adults with AD/HD lead a better life.

Philip Parker, M.D., is a private-practice psychiatrist who treats adults. He has presented at the National Attention Deficit Disorder Association (ADDA) and CHADD conferences about various medication

issues for AD/HD in adults. Dr. Parker is on the Professional Advisory Board of ADDA and is assistant clinical professor of psychiatry at the Wayne State University School of Medicine.

Editor's Note: The article is adapted from the What We Know sheet entitled, "Medication Management for Adults with AD/HD," supported by Cooperative Agreement Number R04/CCR 321831-01 from the Centers for Disease Control and Prevention (CDC). The contents are solely the responsibility of the authors and do not necessarily represent the official views of CDC. The sheet was approved in 2004 by CHADD's Professional Advisory Board. The full version is available at www.help4adhd.org/en/about.

This article first appeared in *Attention!®* magazine, April 2005.

> It is important that your primary care physician be in the loop with your mental health care provider.

Your Vehicle Donation Will Lower Your Taxes and Benefit CHADD

There is an easy and convenient way to donate your used car, truck, RV, SUV, motorcycle or boat to CHADD and get a tax deduction. Through the CHADD National Car Donation Program, all of the work is done for you at no charge: quick towing service, title processing, appraisal (if required), sale at auction or dismantler, accounting and a receipt for tax purposes.

You can make your vehicle donation to CHADD through our partnership with the nonprofit organization Volunteers of America. Visit www.carshelpingpeople.org/chadd for more details and an online application or call toll free at 1-800-948-1414. When making an online donation, please be sure to include the "/chadd" at the end of the Web site address. If phoning in your donation, you must indicate that CHADD is your designated charity for CHADD to benefit.

CHADD chapters are eligible to receive 25 percent of the net proceeds of vehicles donated by members to CHADD National. Any non-member donor is welcome to contact the Development Department at CHADD to designate a chapter to get 25 percent of the net proceeds.

Your vehicle donation will be greatly appreciated and will support the CHADD mission to improve the lives of people affected by Attention-Deficit/Hyperactivity Disorder.

CHADD®
CHILDREN AND ADULTS WITH
ATTENTION-DEFICIT/
HYPERACTIVITY DISORDER